MUSEUM GUIDE

International Maritime Museum Hamburg

KOEHLERS VERLAGSGESELLSCHAFT HAMBURG

Even as an inhabitant of a Hanseatic town, there is truly a lot of seawater in Peter Tamm's blood. He began his career in 1948 as an editor for shipping and navigation and, as chairperson of the board of Axel-Springer Verlag, he was called 'the Admiral'. Already at the age of six he began collecting nautical items, a passion which eventually became the largest private collection for maritime history. Today, visitors from all over the world can admire the collection at the International Maritime Museum in the HafenCity.

The collection comprises 40,000 individual items and more than 1 million photographs. In over 12,000 m^2 of exhibition space, visitors can gaze with admiration at maritime art, learn about marine research, energy technology and fisheries, or follow in the footsteps of the great discoverers and navigators, just to name a few of the museum's exhibit themes. I have often heard of guests from both Germany and abroad that were astounded by the diverse and multifaceted nature of the museum's offerings. With this in mind I wish you an unforgettable visit, and may you always have the famous 'hand's width of water under your keel'.

Yours,

Olaf Scholz

FIRST MAYOR

SURROUNDED BY THE SEA

'It has a thousand colours and a thousand faces', Reinhard Mey sings in his song 'Das Meer'. He closes with words which remind us to be humble before nature: 'We need the sea, but the sea doesn't need us'. Human beings always needed the sea for communication and for trade with other people and nations. How else but by seafaring could distant continents and foreign cultures be discovered, and empires such as the Roman and British empires establish themselves? And where else has the collective 'we' been so important as on ships and on the oceans?
Certainly, many hostilities have been dealt out and many battles have been fought at sea. Tragedies such as the sinking of the 'Titanic' and the 'Wilhelm Gustloff' took place on the water. Pirates robbed, and seafaring conquerors murdered. Still, the seas have overwhelmingly served peaceful purposes and improved the economic prosperity of mankind by means of free trade.
More than two thirds of Earth's surface is covered by water. They influence the climate. They are Nature's most significant reserve of energy, strength and resilience. Environmental control of the oceans is a collective duty of mankind. Maritime history means world history, and it is the history of humanity. The International Maritime Museum Hamburg (IMMH) endeavours to document this aspect of history in a global context, pitting against the zeitgeist and all political influences, and loyal only to the truth.
Since the opening of our Museum in 2008 in the oldest harbour warehouse in the city, we have become one of the leading centres in the world for maritime history, both for visitors from Germany and abroad and for research. Our team of around 40 paid employees and 80 volunteers is proud of its contributions. And we never rest. New exhibits are added almost every day. This

Museum Guide describes what you are able to discover for yourself on over 10,000 m^2 of exhibit space on nine floors. This is an invitation for you to visit us and to get to know our exhibits better. You and your friends are always cordially welcome to our museum.

Yours,

Prof. Peter Tamm

THE MUSEUM
IN YOUR POCKET

The IMMH is a treasure trove providing a wide range of insights into the history of seafaring. It is a history of the relationship between mankind and the sea which has endured for thousands of years. Of course this means that there is a lot to tell about this topic. There are stories of adventurers, craftsmen and cartographers, of technology, vessels in distress, fishing, war and peace, of the hard life on board and of elegant cruise liners.

Finding ways through this diversity is the aim of Museum curators. This is no easy job, since the collection includes more than 100,000 individual items and more than a million photographs. 50,000 miniature models are held in the archives, plus 4,000 paintings and watercolours, hundreds of historical uniforms and tens of thousands of of constructional drawings.

In each chapter of this guide, which is represented on one deck of the museum, the most important exhibits are highlighted. If a visitor doesn't have much time, he or she can concentrate on these exhibits during a visit. The order presented in the exhibits corresponds to a possible walk around the respective deck.

The visitor can of course also simply wander through the decks according to his or her own whims and use the Museum Guide as a reference. Experiencing the entire collection in one visit seems hardly possible. Thus one way that this guide can be used is for supplemental reading after visiting the museum, and to learn interesting facts about Christopher Columbus, the Titanic, the Port of Hamburg, Admiral Nelson and the adventures of underwater research.

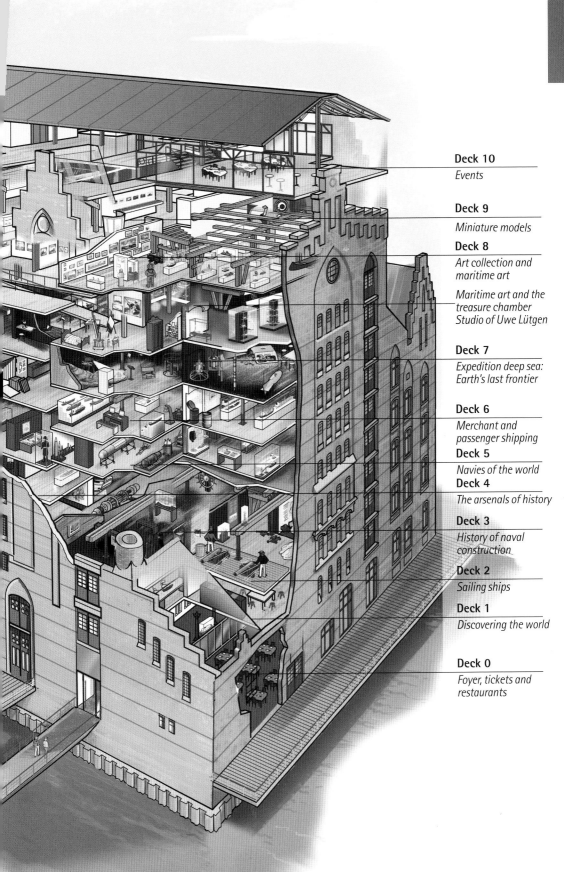

Deck 10
Events

Deck 9
Miniature models

Deck 8
Art collection and maritime art

Maritime art and the treasure chamber Studio of Uwe Lütgen

Deck 7
Expedition deep sea: Earth's last frontier

Deck 6
Merchant and passenger shipping

Deck 5
Navies of the world

Deck 4
The arsenals of history

Deck 3
History of naval construction

Deck 2
Sailing ships

Deck 1
Discovering the world

Deck 0
Foyer, tickets and restaurants

MARITIMES MUSEUM

IN FRONT OF THE MUSEUM
DAR-ES SALAAM-PLATZ ENTRANCE

The museum has two entrances. From the Speicherstadt district, one crosses Dar-es Salaam-Platz, where some large exhibits related to the museum are on display.

Stock anchor
A stock or fisherman's anchor is a weight anchor. It holds the ship not only with its great weight but also through the orientation of the stock and the flukes. If the anchor is pulled upon, the stock (which is at a 90° angle to the flukes) comes to rest horizontally on the bottom. If a greater pull comes onto the anchor, one of the flukes digs into the bottom. Stock anchors count among the oldest anchors. They are particularly suited to clay-rich or sandy seafloors. Because of their size, stock anchors were hung outside on the bow especially of sailing ships.

Patent anchor
In contrast to the weight anchor, the patent anchor buries itself into the sea bottom with two movable flukes in a nearly horizontal motion. A long anchor chain on the bottom ensures this motion. The name of the anchor refers to a patent granted in 1852.

Approach buoy 'Elbe 1'
Approach buoys are navigational aids used at sea. They indicate the beginning of the navigable fairway and are marked with the colours red and white. In the year 2000, the 'Elbe 1' buoy replaced a lightship anchored at a certain position in the mouth of the river Elbe. Lightships had performed their dangerous service at that position since 1816. By the year 2000, 26 seamen on lightships had lost their lives in storms or collisions with other ships. Lightship 'Elbe 1' named 'Bürgermeister O'Swald II' had to endure 50 collisions. After just four years of service, the 'Elbe 1' buoy was replaced in 2004 as part of routine maintenance.

Alte Laterne Holtenau (Südmolenfeuer or South Pier Light)
The Alte Laterne Holtenau, the 'South Pier' or 'Südmole', was a navigational beacon. For nearly one hundred years, from 1895 to 1994, the lamp was located at the Kiel Canal. Then it was replaced by a modern lamp suitable for radar antennae.

IN FRONT OF THE MUSEUM KOREASTRASSE ENTRANCE

There are also items on display on the south forecourt of the Museum at Busanbrücke.

Propeller from tanker 'Maaskerk', Belgium 1975

This massive ship propeller was manufactured as a replacement part for the 170 m long tanker 'Maaskerk'. It has a diameter of 6 metres and weighs 15.5 tons. Two cranes were required to deliver it to the Museum.

24-pounder long gun

The historical guns adjacent on both sides of the Museum's entrance once belonged to the armament of HMS 'Foudroyant'. This ship-of-the-line, built in 1798, served Vice Admiral Horatio Nelson as a flagship from 1799 to 1801.

ENTRANCE AND FOYER

By a passageway you will reach the foyer of our museum. In the foyer are located the cash desk and the 'Wede' bookstore. Wede is offering books on seafaring, sailing, navies, aviation, railways and automobiles. In addition to books, there is an extensive range of miniature models available. Tickets are checked just in front of the lift. Directly behind this area, you will find the courtyard of our museum where more large exhibits are presented.

The forecourt, with a ship propeller and historical ship guns, sets the stage for the exhibits on display.

View of the passageway with model ships, flags and restaurants

The foyer of the Maritime Museum combines historical and modern architecture.

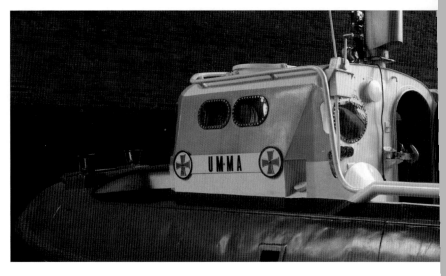

MUSEUM COURTYARD

'Umma 1' shore rescue boat

In 1971–1972 the German Maritime Search and Rescue Service acquired twelve rescue boats of the '7 metre boat'-class. The 'Umma 1' is one of these. First stationed at Heligoland, then at Eckernförde and Damp, this boat's volunteer crew took part in numerous rescue operations. To the right of the 'Umma 1', there is a row of historic Dutch cannons.

Dutch East India Company 75 pounder mortar, Netherlands, 1786

A mortar is an artilleristic device that shoots its ammunition in a high arc, able to reach beyond obstacles. This hanging bronze mortar was cast in 1786 by Cristian Seest in Amsterdam for the Vereenigde Oostindische Compagnie (United Dutch East India Company). With a calibre of 31 cm, it shot explosive bombs weighing around 80 kg. This mortar had been in use at the fortress Batavia (now Jakarta) until the beginning of the 19th century. At that time, Indonesia was a Dutch colony. In 1863, the mortar and other armament was sent

In the courtyard there is a collection of old Dutch cannons

back to the Netherlands. The sailing ship used for the return transport, the 'Willem de Zwijger', unfortunately struck a reef off the coast of east Africa and sank. It wasn't until the 1970s that the bronze mortar was salvaged.

100 pounder mortar, Netherlands, 1748. The standing bronze mortar was cast in 1748 by Cornelis Crans in Hagæ (now The Hague). The front section shows the Dutch royal crest with the inscription VIGILANTE DEO CONFIDENTES (Trusting in a vigilant God). With a calibre of 39 cm, it still shot only stone balls. The mortar had the same fate as the 75 pounder from 1786 displayed here.

30 pounder carronade, Netherlands, 1800 The Carronade, designed in the English style, was cast in the year 1800 by C. Seest in Liège, Belgium for the Batavian Republic's navy. This short-lived republic (1795–1806) was established in the Netherlands under the influence of the French Revolution and maintained its own navy. The short-barrelled carronades, named after the Scottish manufacturer Carron Works, were close combat cannons for classic line-of-battle engagement. The calibre of this carronade is 15.5 cm.

12 pounder cannon, Netherlands, 1614. The bronze barrel with two stylized dolphin handles was cast in 1614 by Iohannis Burgerhuys in Middelburg. Even though the barrel only displays the Dutch royal crest, it can be assumed that it was used on a retourship of the Dutch East India Company. With this relatively long-barrelled cannon with 12 cm diameter a good ballistic

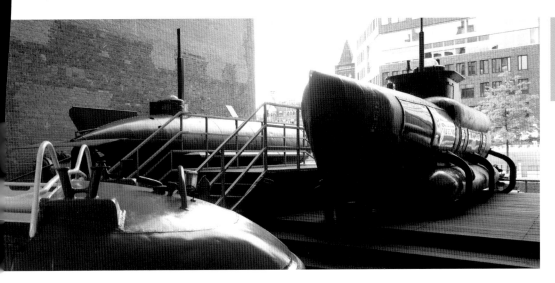

performance was achieved. It is not known if this cannon has ever seen any action.

Dutch East India Company (VOC) 12 pounder cannon, Netherlands, 1740
The 12 pounder bronze barrel was cast in 1740 by Ciprianus Crans Lanszoon in Amsterdam. The Dutch East India Company's insignia can be found on the barrel, with an 'A' for the Admiralty of Amsterdam. The 12 pounder gun was used on Company's heavy retourships, that transported most of the goods from Batavia (now Jakarta) to Europe.

24 pounder cannon, Netherlands, 1615
The bronze barrel is inscribed on the rear section with the insignia ZEELANDIA and the year 1615. It was cast by Iohannes Burgerhuys in Middelburg for the Admiralty of Zeeland. The 14 cm cannon was salvaged from the seafloor. It is assumed that it was part of the armament of a Dutch warship and saw service in one of the three Anglo-Dutch wars in the 17th century.

On the other side of the courtyard, midget submarines and propellers are on display.

Bronze torpedo tube for 45 cm torpedo, Germany, 1905
Since welding technology was not yet common in ship construction in 1905, torpedo tubes were cast from bronze in three parts, attached to each other with threaded bolt connectors. Pressurized air was used to launch torpedoes. Early German torpedo boats had single torpedo tubes on pivots standing on the upper deck. Later, larger torpedo boats and torpedo boat destroyers had two tubes arranged in a V pattern or swiv-

el-mounted in twin tubes on deck. This torpedo tube is a relic of a torpedo boat which has been sunk during World War One.

'Seehund', midget submarine, type 127
Germany from 1944
A total of 285 midget submarinesof the 'Seehund'-type or 'Seal' series were built in 1944–1945. Under the command of the K-Verband small battle units of the Kriegsmarine, the crews were trained at Neustadt in Holstein.
This training boat was salvaged in 2001 south of the island of Fehmarn, along with the remains of both of its crew members. Neither the identity of the soldiers, who were later buried at the Vorwerker Cemetery in Lübeck, nor the cause of the sinking could be determined. Our thoughts are with the deceased. The wartime use of the boat, which from 1st January 1945 was deployed from the Netherlands against the allied supply traffic, resulted in the loss of about one third of the boats. Around 115 'Seehund' drivers lost their lives in these boats. Maximum range: 63 nautical miles submerged; crew: 2 persons

In the courtyard, small U-boats
and a shore rescue boat are on display

The ship propellers on the north exterior wall originally came from U-boats

Bronze busts of well-known discoverers, and maps of their voyages:
Leif Eriksson (c. 970–c. 1020), Zheng He (1371–1433 or 1435), Bartolomeu Diaz (around 1450–1500),
Christopher Columbus (1451–1505), Vasco da Gama (around 1469–1524), Ferdinand Magellan (1480–1521),
James Cook (1728–1779); bronze busts by Ulrich Rölfing

HIGHLIGHTS ON DECK 1

Four crown compasses.
They were hung from the ceiling in the captain's quarters. The master lying in his bed could keep an eye on whether the ship steered the correct course.

Davis quadrant,
angle measuring instrument, 18th century. Using angle measuring instruments, users could navigate along a particular line of latitude on the open sea.

The Sailing and Fighting Instructions or Signals as They are Observed in the Royal Navy of Great Britain.
This code of signals from the early 18th century contains 106 signals with a variety of flags and pennants.

Radio room of a merchant ship
in about 1960. Display uses original objects.

Pilot badges.
Rare badges from pilots.

Atlantis Majoris.
17th century, the first nautical atlas printed in the Netherlands.

De Fransche Neptunus of Nieuwe Atlas van de Zeekaarten.
An elegant, hand-coloured nautical atlas from the late 17th century.

Models of the lighthouses
Roter Sand and Faro de Punta del Hidalgo

Ship command simulator
Ship steering for everybody – in a simulator

DISCOVERY OF THE WORLD: NAVIGATION AND COMMUNICATION

The vastness of the ocean symbolizes the human desire to explore the unknown and make new discoveries. For these endeavours, not only ships are needed, but also instruments for navigation and communication such as compasses, maps, sextants, Morse code devices and signal codes. In ancient times, observations of nature were critically important for navigation. The sun and the stars showed seafarers the way. Today, navigation relies on the most modern technologies: radar, echo sounding and GPS systems. The front part of the floor is reserved for children. In the 'Floating Classroom', we have games, books and handicraft supplies available for young discoverers to use. There is also a model of the 'Queen Mary 2', built from nearly a million Lego bricks. Right next to this, experts in our model construction workshop take care of precious museum objects. You are quite welcome to take a peek over the shoulders of the workshop employees. Of course they are also happy to answer any questions you may have.

1 SPECIAL EXHIBITIONS AREA
Area reserved for special exhibitions.

2 WHAT THE ANCIENTS KNEW
Stars point the way

Astronomy is the oldest science. Even in antiquity, the heavens were systematically observed to determine the time and later the calendar. However, until the invention of the telescope ca. 1600 AD only objects identifiable with the naked eye and positioning instruments could be interpreted. The earliest known observations come from the Near and Far East: from China there are references to eclipses of the sun in the 3rd millennium BC, and there are similar reports from India and Babylon going just as far back in time.

It was absolutely vital for seafarers to know the position and movement of celestial bodies. Anyone who could 'read' the sky could navigate at night by the stars. The constellations – groups of stars with a clearly identifiable pattern – were articularly important. Already in antiquity, constellations from star catalogues were used for navigation. The constellation most well-known worldwide for millennia is the star cluster of the Pleiads, referred to as an independent group in almost every culture. The great Homer also has his hero Odysseus navigate by the Pleiads.

The earth is round

The oldest known portrayals of the earth show our planet as a disk. But already in antiquity, Pythagoras (6th c. BC), Plato (427–347 BC) and Aristotle (389-322 BC) thought that the earth is a sphere. In his treatise 'On the Heavens', Aristotle comments that the shadow of the earth during an eclipse of the moon seems to be circular and that only a sphere creates this effect. A further indication of our planet's spherical form is that the position of the polar star seems to change for the observer depending on the location on earth. And the curvature of the earth can also be inferred from the fact that at sea first the sails of a ship become visible and then its hull. In ca. 220 BC, the Greek scholar Eratosthenes noted that at midday on June 21st (summer solstice) vertical objects cast shadows in Alexandria but do not cast any shadows in Syene (today Assuan), where the sun stands exactly at its zenith at this time. He attributed this phenomenon to the various latitudes on a sphere. Eratosthenes calculated the circumference of the earth with astonishing precision. Claudius Ptolemy (ca. 100–ca. 170 AD) also postulated a spherical earth, although he assumed that it is positioned in the centre of space. In the centu-

ries after Ptolemy, it was the Arabs who refined mathematics and observation techniques and with their translations transmitted classical knowledge to the West. Now, if the earth is a sphere, it is also possible to sail around it.

Claudius Ptolemy's world map

The world map of Claudius Ptolemy dating from the 2nd c. AD contains the geographical knowledge of antiquity and provides details on all places known at that time and their location. An original of this work has not been preserved. It was probably not until the 15th c. that the Ptolemaic 'Instructions' with map supplements came to Europe via scholars as transcripts from Byzantium.

The Ptolemaic world map features an equator and two tropics. The earth is covered with a network of degrees: 180 degrees divide the world from the Canaries in the west to the then known world in the east, 65 degrees divide the north and 25 the south. The map

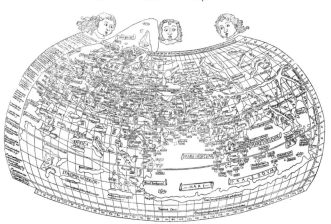

represents an early attempt to project the curved earth on a flat surface. Despite all its errors, Ptolemy's world map provided the basis for the development of reliable nautical charts in the 15th c. Whether Ptolemy did in fact compile the work attributed to him is still a matter of controversy, but this does not diminish its significance, as it marked the beginnings of scientific cartography.

3 THE AGE OF THE FAMOUS DISCOVERERS

They made history with their voyages, filling in the white spots on the world map and discovering new sea routes. They risked their lives and earned fame and fortune if they were successful. 'Was it not from the pleasure which naturally results to a man from his being the first discoverer... this kind of Service would be insupportable', the English captain and navigator James Cook (1728–1779) once said. Still, it wasn't only the personal challenges that motivated these men. Their voyages needed to be financed, and the patrons who supplied the funds typically had political, economic, religious or military interests. More than two thousand years before the Portuguese and Spanish set out to look for the sea route to India, the Greeks and Phoenicians had already dared to venture out into unknown waters. The names of these voyagers have mostly been lost to time. In contrast, those men who searched for unknown lands and sea routes at the beginning of modern times, in the so-called European Age of Discovery, have made it into history books. In the service of their patrons, they searched for shorter trade routes, and prepared the way for the establishment of market monopolies and the expansion of territories. The competition for influence and power could no longer be stopped. This eventually led to worldwide conflicts in the colonial era.

Leif Eriksson (c. 970–c. 1020)

The Viking Leif Eriksson (Leiv Eirikssön), son of the Greenland explorer Eirik Raude (Erik the Red), is regarded as the discoverer of North America. He probably was in fact the first European to land ca. 1001 on the coast of North America, reaching Newfoundland (according to another theory, he went as far as Massachusetts). He called the country he set foot on Vinland. However, he did not discover it. The first man to see the coast of America was the Icelander Bjarni Herjólfsson. On a voyage from Iceland to Greenland in 985, he had been driven by currents off to the west, where he sighted unknown land – most likely the coast of Labrador. 'Our voyage will one day seem unwise, because none of us had previously been in Greenland's waters,' Bjarni Herjólfsson is said to have commented on his involuntary voyage of discovery. After his return to Greenland, his reports attracted the interest of Leif Eriksson. Along with 35 companions, Eriksson departed in spring 1001 in the direction of the coast sighted by

Herjólfsson. For a year he and his companions wandered through the interior of the newly discovered land, where he eventually decided to settle, encouraging others to join him from Greenland. The men of the north were impressed most by the wild grapes after which they named the land they had found.

Zheng He (1371–1433 or 1435)

China boasts a long seafaring tradition. As early as the Han dynasty (206 BC–220 AD), Chinese ships were sailing to India. The western world found out about the famous Chinese admiral and seafarer Cheng Ho and his amazing voyages only in the 1930s, when a stone pillar with an inscription recounting his expeditions was discovered in a town in the province of Fujian. Cheng Ho was born into a Moslem family in the province of

Yunnan. He was captured by Ming soldiers when he was 11. He was castrated at the age of 13 and then served at the household of the later Emperor Cheng Tsu, who had the highly talented youngster trained in the arts of war and diplomacy. Appointed an admiral in 1403, Cheng Ho commanded a fleet of treasure ships for exploring the waters around China. He undertook seven expeditions in the Pacific and Indian Oceans and in the Persian Gulf between 1405 and 1433. He visited more than 30 countries from Asia to Africa with his fleet of over 60 vessels, which included junks up to 84 metres long. As many as 27,000 persons participated in these voyages. Cheng Ho's fleet was thus the largest to sail the oceans up to that time. His emperor called on him later to journey to the countries beyond the horizon, venturing to the very end of the world, according to the inscription on the stone column.

Bartolomeu Diaz

(about 1450–1500)
The Portuguese planned to sail around the southern tip of Africa to find the sea route to India. They already knew

the west coast of Africa up to the present Cape Cross when in 1487 Portugal's King John II commissioned Bartholomew Diaz to complete the exploration project.

We hardly know anything about Diaz before he embarked on the voyage of discovery that made him famous. He departed from Lisbon in August 1487 with three small ships. His voyage was to take him via the Cape of Good Hope into the Indian Ocean. Diaz sailed along the west coast of Africa as far as the present Cardowberg, where a storm forced him to turn to the south-west. He was then able to proceed on an easterly course again and when after some days no land came into sight he concluded that Africa does not form a barrier between the Atlantic and Indian Ocean and that he had rounded the continent's southern tip. Diaz had thereby opened up for Portugal the gateway to the Indian Ocean, but he failed to achieve his aim of being the first European to find the sea route to India, as his officers mutinied, compelling him to turn back. Twelve years later, Diaz commanded one of the mighty ships of the fleet of Pedro Cabral on an expedition to India. On May 24th 1500, this encountered a heavy storm near the Cape of Good Hope, and four vessels – including that of Diaz – were lost with their crews.

Christopher Columbus (1451–1506)

At the age of 30, Christopher Columbus, a native of Genoa, resolved to find the sea route to India by sailing westwards – in contrast to the Portuguese plan of reaching the Far East via the Cape of Good Hope. He eventually enlisted the support of Ferdinand and Isabella of Spain to enable him to realise his great ambition. Columbus departed with one não and two caravels, the 'Santa Maria', 'Pinta' and 'Niña', on August 3rd 1492. He intended to sail westwards on the latitude of the Canaries. On October 12th 1492, he landed on one of the Bahama Islands – Guanahani, as it was later established. He believed that it lay before India.

Columbus carried on to Cuba, which he took for a peninsula off the Chinese coast. Sailing from the Cuban east coast, he discovered an island, which he named 'Española' (later Hispaniola). On his return home, he was received with great honours and appointed Viceroy of India. Columbus undertook three more voyages. On the second, he colonised Hispaniola, while during the third he anchored for the first time close to the American coast, off Venezuela. On his fourth voyage, he intended to seek a passage through the newly discovered continent. Despite his tremendous achievement, Columbus died a broken man on May 20th 1506 after having lost his privileges following disturbances in the colony of Hispaniola. To the very end of his life, he continued to believe that he had been in India.

Vasco da Gama (around 1649–1524)

Bartholomew Diaz returned to Lisbon after his expedition along the African west coast in December 1488.

He had ventured around the southern tip of Africa into the Indian Ocean. However, Vasco da Gama was commissioned by the king of Portugal to find the sea route to India once and for all. An aristocrat by birth, da Gama was soldier, seaman and diplomat. He had a fleet of particularly well-built ships, which were also armed for offensive operations. On July 8th 1497, he departed from Lisbon and reached the southern tip of Africa, where Diaz had been forced to turn back ten years previously. Da Gama proceeded with

difficulty along the African east coast to Malindi in today's Kenya. Its sultan provided him with a pilot – probably Ahmed ben Madjid, the most experienced navigator of the Indian Ocean in his day – for the last leg of the voyage. Vasco da Gama reached his destination in May 1498. He concluded an initial trading agreement with the local ruler in Calicut on the south-west coast of India. Then he started back, taking three times as long for the return as for the outward voyage, as he had to contend with lulls in the wind, head winds and the scourge of scurvy. He eventually made a triumphal entry in Lisbon in September 1499. Portugal acquired the status of a world power thanks to this voyage. Vasco da Gama sailed three more times to India, where he died in 1524, four months after assuming office as viceroy.

Ferdinand Magellan (1480–1521)

Ferdinand Magellan (Magalhães) departed from Sanlúcar de Barrameda in Spain on his epic voyage of discovery to the Spice Islands on September 20th 1519. This was to become the very first circumnavigation of the globe. Magellan, however, did not live to return to Spain.

Like Columbus, the Portuguese Magellan could undertake his voyage only thanks to the support of the Spanish king: he won the enthusiastic backing of Charles I (later Emperor Charles V) for his project for reaching the famed Spice Islands by sailing west, which presupposed finding a way around South America. The young monarch provided five caravels, 250 crew members and provisions for the expedition. Magellan proceeded via Madeira along the west coast of Africa, over the Atlantic to Brazil and on to the mouth of the Rio de La Plata. Sailing along the coast, which was at that time unknown, Magellan sought a passage that would enable him to reach the other side of America. After a severe winter and an open mutiny, on October 21st 1520 he discovered at Cape Virgin the eastern end of the strait that today bears his name. The passage to the

other side of the world took 27 days. Magellan named the calm sea he saw 'Mar Pacifico' – the peaceful. In March, he reached Cebù in the Philippines, where he became involved in a tribal conflict and was killed. The great mariner's mission was eventually completed by his successor Juan Sebastian del Cano.

James Cook (1728–1779)

The Englishman James Cook, born on October 27th 1728 in Marton, Yorkshire, began his seafaring career on a collier at the age of 19. He joined the Royal Navy in 1755 and in 1768 was appointed for the first time to head an expedition with various objectives, including finding the unknown southern continent 'terra australis'. Via Tahiti and New Zealand, Cook reached the east coast of Australia, which he claimed for the British crown. On his second expedition (1772-75), Cook sailed via Easter Island, New Caledonia and New Hebrides as far as the Antarctic,

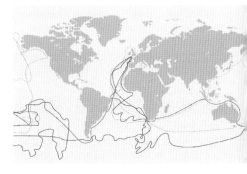

reaching South Georgia and the South Sandwich Islands. On his third expedition from 1776, he explored the north-west coast of America as far as West Alaska and Kamtchatka and sought in vain for the North-West Passage. On February 14th 1779, Cook was killed in a skirmish with natives on Hawaii, where he had intended to spend the winter.

James Cook found out more about the Pacific than any previous explorer, roaming that huge ocean from Tahiti to Siberia. He sailed around the globe three times. In the south he crossed the polar circle three times. Thanks to Cook, the world became aware of the enormous size of the oceans. The first map of the dangerous west coast of North America as far as Bering Strait was made on his last voyage. The great discoverer's achievements also included systematically overcoming the very serious problem of scurvy.

4 THE BEGINNINGS OF NAVIGATION

Sounding line The sounding line is probably the oldest instrument for measuring depth. Already around 448 BC, the Greek historian Herodotus refers to the use of the 'lead', and the Bible also mentions how sailors 'sounded'.

The simple sounding line consists of a measuring line, at the end of which a lead weight hangs, hence the designations 'lead' or 'sounding line'. Strings are attached to the line at regular intervals on which the depth is read off. The instrument could only be used near land and in shallow waters, however.

The sounding line had another function: the hollow sinker was filled with tallow, on which ground particles such as sand or small stones adhered, providing information on the characteristics of the seabed.

'The following is a general description of the physical features of Egypt. If you take a cast of the lead a day's sail off-shore, you will get eleven fathoms [about 20 meters], muddy bottom – which shows how far out the silt from the river extends.' (Book II of The History of Herodotus, verse 5)

Log The log serves to measure a ship's speed. The early hand logs consisted of a flat, triangular piece of wood weighted with lead that was thrown into the water and with the weight floated on the spot. A line with knots at regular intervals was secured on the piece of wood. A sand-glass was used to measure a specific period of time, and then it was determined how much line had run off during this time. This method could not achieve any exact results, and the approximate speed of the ship could be determined only during the period of the measurement. However, the expression knots (kn) for designating the speed of a ship is still used today:
1 knot = 1 sea mile per hour.
A refinement of the hand log was the patent log with speed counter, using a propeller attached to the log line for towing behind the vessel with its speed of rotation displayed on a dial indicator, in nautical miles. It was thus possible to read off the speed at any time. The first logs with speed counters were produced by Edward Massey, who took out a patent for his invention in 1802. From 1851, patent logs indicating tenths of miles, miles and tens of miles were produced by Thomas Walker according to the same principle. Today ships are equipped with pitometer logs, which measure speed by the water pressure in a cylinder attached to the stem.

Sounding line This old device for the measurement of depth and bottom characteristics in nearshore and shallow waters consists of a lead weight and a line with threads added for reading off the depth.

Hand log

The speed of the ship can be measured with this log. The early chip logs consisted of a piece of wood weighted with lead (here, supplemented) to which a line was attached. The flat piece of wood was thrown into the water. Due to its weight, it remained in more or less the same place in the water. Knots were tied into the line at regular intervals. To determine the speed, the length of line that runs out during a certain time period is determined.

Walker's Patent Harpoon Shiplog

England, end of 19th century. The patent log was towed by a log line. The rotations of the propeller are conveyed to the revolution counter, from which the speed of the ship could be read off.

Walker's patent log 'Cherub III' England, early 20th century.
With this patent log, the revolution counter was no longer a part of the float's body, but rather it was separately fixed to the rail. A flywheel transferred the rotation of the propeller to the revolution counter.

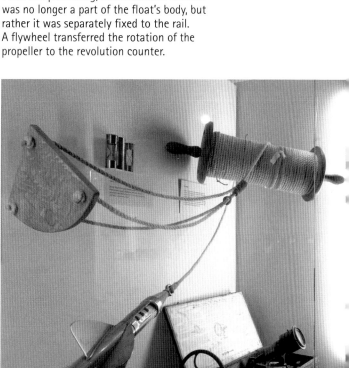

Sand hourglasses Quarter minute and half minute glass

For speed measurement using the log method, hourglasses ensured that the time intervals for the measurement were equal and therefore comparable to each other.

MAGNETISM

Like most rocky planets, the earth is a large magnet, with a magnetic field running from south to north. All small magnets orient themselves along the field lines between the magnetic poles of the earth. The compass needle is also such a small magnet and thus – floating freely or positioned on water – exactly shows the direction of the local field line. It points to the magnetic North Pole, which however is not identical with the geographical North Pole. The angle between magnetic polarity and geographical polarity is the so-called compass variation. Even in antiquity, it was known that certain iron ores (magnetite) have a magnetising effect. Large deposits of these magnet stones were found in the vicinity of the town of Magnesia in Asia Minor, on the present west coast of Turkey. The Chinese were probably the first to make use of the characteristics of magnetic stone for determining direction. There are already references to a magnetic compass in the form of a magnetite spoon freely floating on a disk between the 5th and 3rd c. BC.

Compass The compass was probably introduced in Europe via the Arabs from China in the 10th c. There is evidence that it was used for shipping in Europe in the 14th c. Almost only dry compasses were used on ships up to 1800. Liquid compasses – with needle and compass rose floating in a casing filled with liquid that dampens the movements – became common in the first half of the 19th c.

Two disturbances, the deflection of the compass by iron on board and magnetic compass variation, can lead to display errors. It was already known at an early date that the geographical and magnetic North Pole are not identical and that this has to be taken into consideration when calculating a ship's course. It was known in the 18th c. that iron distorts a ship's compass. This became an acute problem with the construction of iron ships in the 19th c. A solution was the wooden compass binnacle, fitted with side iron spheres and soft iron bars in the casing to offset most of the deviation. The gyro compass introduced in 1904 works without magnetic

Binnacle

distortions. The axis of its rotating gyroscope driven by electricity is guided by the earth's rotation in a northerly direction and points to the geographical North Pole. The gyro compass is thus independent of the earth's magnetic field.

Dry compass with bearing attachment
Portugal, 1783
Signed 'Simao Antonio. Da Roza Pinheiro'. The compass is hand-painted and mounted with gimbals in its wooden case. The closable bearing attachment could be used to take the bearing of a navigation mark.

Binnacle, compass with compensating spheres on its sides, mounted on a column made of non-magnetic material. A lantern illuminates the compass housing from within the stand.

Crown compass, Denmark, 18th century
Signed: 'Peder Nielsen & Brenöe København'. The housing is based on the pattern of the Danish crown jewels.

Crown compass, Netherlands, 1795, signed: 'Willem en Albert'

Crown compass, Germany, around 1780 signed: 'John Hinrn Saegelken Bremen'

Crown compass, Netherlands, around 1800, signed: 'Johannes Akey Com Kompassmaker Tot Amsterdam'

Textbooks on navigation

Dell Arcano del Mare
Robert Dudley, Florence, 1647
'Dell Arcano del Mare' means: 'On the Mystery of the Sea'

Breue compendio de la sphera y de la arte de navegar
Martin Cortez Sevilla, 1551, M. Cortez compiled a 'Brief Compendium of the Sphere [Earth] and the Art of Navigation'.

Arte de Navegar, em que se ensinao as regras praticas, ...
Manoel Pimentel, Lisbon, 1762
A work on 'The Art of Navigation, in which the practical rules are taught'.

Sailing by the stars
Homer's 'Odyssey' contains numerous descriptions of seafaring in antiquity. One passage shows that Greek mariners already navigated by the stars in the 12th century BC: 'Odysseus ... used his seamanship to keep his boat with the steering-oar ... and never closed his eyes in sleep, but kept them on the Pleiads, or watched Bootes slowly set, or the Great Bear, nicknamed the Wain, which always wheels round in the same place and looks across at Orion the Hunter with a wary eye. It was this constellation, the only one which never bathes in Ocean's Stream, that the wise goddess Calypso had told him to keep on his left hand as he made across the sea.'
The oldest methods of astronomical navigation include one probably used even in prehistory. Seafarers moved away from the coast to head for a particular destination by using a star to guide them. On clear nights, they navigated by the only fixed point in the northern sky discernible to the human eye, the polar star. If this was always to be seen above the same place on the ship, the mariners could be certain that they were moving straight ahead. By the following morning, the coast that was being steered for had to be in sight, as the direction in which the vessel was moving could be estimated only approximately with the position of the constantly moving sun. The polar star was called 'Leidarstiarna', 'leitesterne' and 'Scip steorra', meaning 'guiding star' or 'ship star'.

Navigational instruments for measuring angles
Before instruments for measuring angles between horizon and astronomical bodies were invented, seafarers found their way across the open sea by the stars, as well as by using a log and a sand-glass and observing the swell of the sea. The compass probably also came into use in the West in the Middle Ages. Mariners determined their course by 'dead reckoning': the place of departure, speed and quarter were noted in order to ascertain the section of the voyage during a watch, and when transferred to paper and connected with one another these showed the distance covered. However, these methods were not very precise.
An instrument for measuring angles was required to enable seafarers to navigate on the open sea along a specific latitude. With this, mariners could take a bearing on the polar star and horizon at night and then read off

Highlight: Crown compasses are also known as hanging compasses or 'spies'. Often richly ornamented, they hung from the ceiling in the captain's quarters. This was so that the captain could follow whether the helmsmen on the deck were correctly steering the ordered course. Since they were read from below, the positions of east and west are swapped on the compass rose.

the elevation angle between them. From the 15th century, tables that pre-calculated the positions of the planets and stars helped sailors compute the sun's altitude by day. The oldest angle-measuring instruments include the astrolabe, which the Arabs introduced in the Mediterranean region, quadrant, Jacob's staff and Davis quadrant (back staff), from which the octant and sextant were developed. Angles of altitude were read off in degrees, minutes of arc and seconds of arc. In the 16th century, navigation was still so imprecise that ships could drift off course by some 30 nautical miles. A seafarer needed to be able to calculate both longitude and latitude in order to pinpoint a position at sea.

Mariner's astrolabe One of the oldest angle-measuring instruments for navigators is the marine astrolabe. Two sights were attached to its swivelling pointer arm (alidade). At night, the star the bearings of which were being taken had to be seen through both sights, and then the angle of elevation could be read off on the graduation of the ring. During the day, the device was left hanging freely and the alidade set so that sunlight fell through the upper sight directly on the lower.

Mariner's astrolabe
(reconstructed) Angle-measuring instrument. Reconstructed from a 17th century artifact found in wreckage. The mariner's astrolabe was developed from the astrolabes used in observatories, which with their closed frames had too much surface area to be used in heavy winds.

Jacob's staff The Jacob's staff (or backstaff) was described for the first time in 1342. For measuring, the cross staff was moved on the longitudinal staff until it stood between the visible horizon and the star. The angle of elevation was then read off on the graduated scale of the longitudinal staff. On Jacob's staffs with several cross staffs, the one covering the required measuring area was used.

Jacob's staff (reconstructed), Angle-measuring instrument
The term 'Jacob's staff' refers to the similarity of the device to the constellation Orion, which was also called 'Jacobus Major' in the Middle Ages. The shape of the instrument resembled the pilgrim's staff of the apostle Jacob.

Davis quadrant The Davis quadrant (named after John Davis, 1527-1605) was helpful for taking a bearing of the sun because the user did not have to look directly into the light. He looked through the sight of the lower graduated arc (limb) to the slit of the horizon sight (H) until he identified the visible horizon in the slit. The shadow sight (S) on the upper limb was moved until its shadow edge fell on the upper edge of the horizon slit. The values read off on the scales of the two limbs were added.

Davis quadrant Angle-measuring instrument, England, 1725. Manufacturer: William Clarke
The three sights or vanes (sighting, horizon and shadow) were added later.

Reflecting octant The reflecting octant (1/8 of a circle), designed by John Hadley in 1730, was more precise than the Davis quadrant. The user looked through the sight until he could see the visible horizon through the opposite horizon sight. He moved the alidade, on which a mirror was fixed, until the reflected celestial body also appeared in the horizon sight. The value was read off on the limb. Hadley's octant had a measuring area of 90 degrees.

Reflecting octant Angle-measuring instrument England, c. 1750
Made by Spencer Browning & Rust, London

Reflecting octant Angle-measuring instrument England, 1841
Made by Gray J. & Keen, Strand, Liverpool

Reflecting sextant The reflecting sextant (1/6 of a circle) with a measuring area of 120 degrees was developed from the reflecting octant. The basic principle remained the same. The first reflecting sextant was produced by John Bird in 1759.

Vernier sextant, Angle-measuring instrument England, 1890. Made by Lee George & Son, Portsmouth
On the case lid there is a certificate of inspection from Kew Observatory, August 1890. There is a vernier scale on the pivoting pointer (alidade), i.e. an additional scale for more precise angle readings.

Chronometer, Russia, 2nd half 19th century
Made by Ericsson, St. Petersburg
Mounted on gimbals in its wooden housing. Chronometers are very precise clocks. Their development was spurred by navigational needs. Knowing the exact time in combination with the elevation angle of a celestial body the geometrical longitude can be determined.

Vernier sextant, Angle-measuring instrument Germany, 1908. Made by C. Plath, Hamburg
There is a vernier scale on the pivoting pointer (alidade), i.e. an additional scale for more precise angle readings.

Positioning at sea:
Latitude and Longitude
Every competent navigator can determine latitude with an angle-measuring instrument. At the beginning of the 17th c., however, even experienced captains could only estimate their position on the open sea, as this presupposed knowing both latitude and longitude. The latter could not be computed. It was known that the exact time plays an important role: at the time when the position was being determined the local time at the observer's position and the local time at a reference point had to be known. The longitude can be calculated from the difference of both times. The enormous significance of finding a solution to the problem of determining longitude is indicated by the huge prize money offered for it by the Board of Longitude appointed by the British parliament. The reward of £ 20,000 was rather more than an ordinary worker's annual earnings at that time – a paltry £ 10. High prizes were also offered by other governments. Two independent procedures for determining longitude, using moon distances and mechanical clocks, were developed parallel to one another.

Two methods to determine latitude: Lunar distance and chronometer

The method of using moon distances initially seemed to be particularly promising.

Moon distances are designated as the angle distances between the moon and other fixed stars and planets, which change quickly and can therefore be read like a kind of 'celestial clock'. At sea, moon distances were measured with angle-measuring instruments.

The observation time was then compared with the Greenwich Time relevant for the measured constellation. This time was given in tables of nautical almanacs. The longitude of the location could be computed from the time difference.

The Göttingen astronomer Tobias Meyer (1723-62) made the basic calculations for assessing observed moon distances.

Working at the same time as Meyer, the English clockmaker John Harrison (1693-1776) designed a mechanical clock that gives the exact time irrespective of ship movements and temperature fluctuations on board a vessel. This was the chronometer. The clock is set at the time of a reference point – today generally Greenwich Mean Time. When noon is determined by the peak of the sun on the spot, the time difference to the reference point is established and from this the longitude for the current location is calculated. Harrison won the competition for finding the best method for determining longitude.

Determination of geographic latitude with the sextant

In this exhibit there is a hands-on station, where the visitor can measure latitude using a model of a sextant and a graphical representation of the zenith of the sun.

5 COMMUNICATION AT SEA

Direct communication between the shore and ships at sea was not possible until the end of the 19th c. Only vessels near the coast could be contacted with light, smoke, noise or flag signals or occasionally with carrier pigeons. Ships that were at sea within sight or earshot of one another communicated via megaphone, flag signals or later also semaphore or light signals or by transferring personnel. All known means of communication could be used only over short distances. Seafarers were often cut off from the outside world for a very long time as soon as they departed on long voyages. Only with the aid of wireless technology could the endless spaces of the oceans be bridged – with wireless telegraphy (Morse), radiotelephony and satellite radio. Today complex computer-supported management and information systems are used for communications.

Signal books are used to standardise communications at sea via visual, noise and radio signals. They specify the transmission of signals with signal flags and the semaphore alphabet, Morse and radio alphabet.

The 'Black Book of the Admiralty' dating from the early 14th c. is the oldest collection of signals for fleets of sailing ships. A treatise on signalling with pennants, lanterns, trumpets and cannons was compiled by the admiral of the Dukes of Burgundy in the 15th c. And in his work 'Architectura navalis' (1629), Josephum Furttenbach describes various flags and their meaning. New instructions for the flag signals for fleet command were issued in England in 1703. The first 'Code of Signals' for the merchant navy was compiled in 1817 by Captain Frederick Marryat (1792-1848) and used by various countries. A copy of it was on the inventory list of the sailing corvette 'Merkur' of the first German Federal Fleet (1848). The International Code of Signals of the British Board of Trade of 1857 registering nearly 70,000 signals became the basis for communications at sea between ships of all countries. Germany oriented itself to this in the 'Signalbuch der Kauffahrteischiffe aller Nationen' (1870). It became generally valid only with the 1901 edition listing close on 500,000 signals.

Signal Book for Admiral of the Red, White and Blue Fleet Squadrons

England, around 1760. Publisher: British Admiralty. Signal book for the commanders of the three British squadrons.

Plates descriptive of The Maritime Flags of All Nations England, 1829
Author: John William Norie

Norie's overview of the maritime flags of all nations was the first international documentation of flag-flying on ships. At the time, there were still no standardized rules for the exchange of messages using flags. These were first established in 1901 in the International Code of Signals.

The Sailing and Fighting Instructions or Signals as They are Observed in the Royal Navy of Great Britain England, 1714
Author: Jonathan Greenwood

Hand-written manuscript with coloured illustrations of day and night signals. The code of signals contains 106 signals with twelve different flags and pennants as well as illustrations of ships using the signals of the 'Fighting Instructions'.

Sailing and Fighting Instructions for His Majesty's Fleet, England, 1714
Publisher: British Admiralty

Code of signals with sailing and fighting instructions for the British Navy.

Code of Signals
England, 1841
Author: Frederick Marryat

The 'Code of Signals for the use of vessels employed in the Merchant Service' by Captain Marryat was used from 1817 to 1870. The signal book for the Merchant Navy represents an international regulation, since during this period it was used not only by England, but also by other nations.

The 1931 International Code of Signals
England, 1932; Publisher: His Majesty's Stationery Office. The International Code of Signals, since its 1901 edition the International Code of Signals defines the meaning of letter codes for safety and navigation purposes. It has since been revised many times. Signals are conveyed optically, acoustically and electronically.

Signalbuch der Kriegsmarine (Code of Signals of the Kriegsmarine)
Germany 1940; publisher: Oberkommando der Kriegsmarine (High Command of the Kriegsmarine). Separate codes of signals for the navy and the merchant navy existed in many countries already at a very early stage. As the enemy had to be prevented from getting to know the meaning of the letter codes the cover of this Code of Signals of the German Navy is weighted with lead so that it would sink quickly in case of need.

Maritime signal flag alphabet
Flag alphabets are used to exchange messages between ships at sea optically, i.e. via signal flags. There are both international and national flag alphabets. Each letter is represented with its own flag showing a specific colour and design. There are also flags for numbers and special flags. All flags of the flag alphabet have further meanings. These special signals are given as one-, two- or three-letter signals. For example, the flag 'B' of the international flag alphabet means: 'I am loading, unloading or carrying dangerous goods'; 'O' means: 'Man overboard'; 'GQ' means: 'Cannot come to help because of bad weather'; and 'MAA' means: 'Urgently request medical assistance'. Signals with more than three letters give details of e.g. bearing, date, time and position. Signals are seldom given with more than four flags at the same time. The identification signals of ships consist of four letters and are

J.W. Norie:
Plates descriptive of The Maritime Flags of All Nations, England, 1829

Signal flag set
(in original boxes),
Germany, 1960s

given in special lists. In contrast to the flag alphabet, the semaphore alphabet gives letters with two identical flags. Different positions of the flags signify different letters.

Radio technology
Wireless technology revolutionised marine communications, as it made it possible for the first time to contact ships out of sight.

Wireless technology is based on electro-magnetic waves. Its possibility was already theoretically predicted by the Scottish physicist James Clerk Maxwell (1831-1879), who drew on the work of the Englishman Michael Faraday (1791-1867) on the magnetic and electric force field. In the 1880s, the Hamburg physicist Heinrich Rudolf Hertz (1857-94) furnished experimental proof: he showed that under the influence of alternating electric fields sparks jump between the ends of an open wire coil. On the basis of this phenomenon, the research area was initially called 'spark telegraphy'. From 1896, the

Italian physicist Guglielmo Marconi (1874-1937) experimented with electromagnetic waves to establish radio links over longer distances, first over 5 km and then in 1899 over the English Channel. The first radio transmission over the Atlantic was made in 1901. Since then, Marconi has been regarded as the founder of wireless communications. The Wireless Telegraph and Signal Company that Marconi established hired out the new technology mainly to shipowners and light-house operators.

View of the radio room of a commercial ship in about 1960
The radio room is one of the most import-ant rooms on board a ship. This room holds the radio equipment, including senders, receivers and auxiliary equipment. The room is manned around the clock by a wireless operator.

6 PILOTAGE ELECTRONIC NAVIGATION
Since the beginnings of seafaring, ships have continually been involved in accidents near land and when heading for ports because shipmasters do not know the particular sea and estuary area. Pilotage is thus as old as shipping itself. Initially, local fishermen familiar with the locality showed ships the way. In the 16th c., captains were provided with pilots. They documented their knowledge of sea and route conditions in order to use them later or pass them on. There is evidence of a pilot system at this time among the then leading seafaring countries, England, the Netherlands, Portugal and Spain.

At the beginning of the 17th c., the first statutory regulations for German sea areas were issued by German sovereign ter-ritories or Hanseatic League cities. The pilots

Highlight:
Radio room of a merchant ship, around 1960. Reproduced with original items.

formed fraternities and their registration was under state control. Initially, they rowed over to the ships that required their services. Soon they used small manoeuvrable sailing boats. With the advent of industrialisation, steam-driven pilot boats with auxiliary sails were deployed until the introduction of the diesel engine.

Even today, accidents occur when persons transfer from one ship to another, particularly in a heavy seaway. The SWATH hull design (Small Waterplane Area Twin Hull) and trimming capabilities developed only very recently reduce the difference in movement between a cargo ship and a pilot boat.

Pilot flag, Great Britain, 180 x 110 cm
The national flag with a white, wide lower border serves as a pilot flag. If it is hoisted, it means: 'pilot requested'.

Other pilotage signals:
According to the 'International Code of Signals', a pilot can be requested with the flags G or PT. At night, a blue light is shown every 15 minutes or a white light is shown at short intervals just above the bulwark. This light should be visible for a minute each time.

Training of pilots
The road to the career of a 'pilot' is long. In total, it lasts about ten years. First the training as a 'Captain for worldwide seafaring with no nautical restrictions' must be completed. After at least two years of seagoing service, with the captain's license without restrictions, the aspiring pilot can apply with the government authorities for maritime or harbour pilotage. The training for pilotage then lasts another eight months.

From the estate of a pilot
Germany, mid-20th century/2nd half of 20th century
Classroom notebooks: notebooks with handwritten lecture notes on the subject of nautical science
'Distances': Notebooks with handwritten and machine-printed entries on distances between destinations worldwide, expressed in nautical miles (NM).

Pilotage rules for the Warnemünde Rostock harbour, 1802

Hamburg pilot schooner 'Elbe 5'
1:50 scale model
Built in 1884 by H.C. Stülcken (Sohn) in Hamburg, this pilot schooner remained in service for 40 years at the mouth of the Elbe. In 1924 it was sold to the Rickmers company and six years later to some private owners in the US. It was named 'Wander Bird' and later on served as floating accomodation. On 8 October 2002, 'Elbe 5' sailed into her home waters again. The Hamburg Maritime Foundation had bought the historic pilot schooner. It now sails as a museum ship.
Model maker: Waldemar Rademann

Pilot boat 'Grimmershörn'
1:50 scale model
Pilot boats transfer pilots from the pilot station or station ship to their assignments. The 'Grimmershörn' was built in 1952 by Hansa Stahl- & Schiffbau GmbH in Cologne-Deutz for the maritime service in Cuxhaven and used as a pilot boat at the Cuxhaven station.
Model maker: Waldemar Rademann

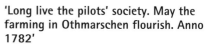

'Long live the pilots' society. May the farming in Othmarschen flourish. Anno 1782'

The farmers of Othmarschen (a small village in the vicinity of Hamburg) gifted this work to the pilots of Oevelgönne. It was an expression of gratitude to the pilots for fetching their hay from the fertile fields on the other side of the Elbe.

'Mark Twain!' was what the pilots on the boats on the Mississippi exclaimed when the sounding line immersed up to a knot marking two fathoms, which meant that the ship had 3.65 m of water under its keel and was in no danger of grounding.

One of the pilots on the Mississippi was Samuel Langhorne Clemens. He began his career in 1857. 'A pilot, in those days, was the only unfettered and entirely independent human being that lived in the earth,' he recalled later. 'In truth, every man and woman and child has a master; but in the day I write of, the Mississippi pilot had none. The moment that the boat was under way in the river, she was under the sole and unquestioned control of the pilot. He received commands from nobody, he promptly resented even the merest suggestions. Indeed, the law of the United States forbade him to listen to commands or suggestions, rightly considering that the pilot necessarily knew better how to handle the boat than anybody could tell him.'

Samuel Langhorne Clemens stood on the pilot's bridge for four years and enjoyed his

Highlight:
Pilot insignia
Rare pilot service badges

Maritime pilot insignia

Early 19th century – 1930s. Pilots wore a pilot's insignia (also called a pilot's badge) on their jackets while performing their duties. It was a service badge and had the function of an ID card. Imprinting of monograms and bearer numbers was the exception rather than the rule.

If the pilot retired, the badge had to be returned. Pilot insignia were common until the 1930s.

'Piloted Ships'

From the estate of a pilot: notebook with handwritten entries on ships piloted. Germany, 1952–1970s.

Telescopes on board

Seafarers always need to see farther than they can with the naked eye – to enable them to navigate around obstacles for example or interpret flag signals correctly. The telescope was used since the time of Galileo Galilei, but various problems with it remained unsolved until the end of the 18th c. Lenses with short focal lengths yielded very distorted pictures. Greater magnification could be achieved only by extending the focal lengths of the lens: eyepieces could be extended to up to ten telescope tubes. In 1757, the British optician Peter Dollond (1731–1820) discovered a method of almost entirely eliminating the distortions by using lenses made of different types of glass. Considerable magnification could now also be achieved with short focal lengths. Another problem, however, remained: increasing magnification leads to a restriction of the field of vision, thus making it difficult on a swaying ship to take a bearing on a distant independence on the Mississippi. He later became a writer and called himself – Mark Twain.

Radio direction finding and radio positioning are used to determine the location of a ship by using radio waves. For radio direction finding, antennae having directional properties are used to determine the direction of signal-transmitting radio beacons. By locating several transmitting beacons with known geographic locations, the intersection of the two directions could be used to determine the location of the ship. The directional properties of antennae were first discovered in the 19th century. The first radio direction finders suitable for on-board use didn't appear until the 1920s, however. The favourable propagation properties of low-frequency radio waves enabled ships to locate transmitting beacons at great distances, and determine their own location with the assistance of a compass.

The **Decca navigation system** is a radio navigation system. It uses radio waves for position determination at sea. It was developed during the Second World War by the British company of the same name. The Decca system was used for the first time at during the landings of the Allied forces in Normandy at the beginning of June 1944. The range of this radio system was limited to 250-400 nautical miles. A Decca radio transmitter chain requires a master station and three subsidiary stations (slaves). At least three transmitters, whose position is known, each emit a signal simultaneously. The recipient can determine his position by comparing the signal transit times.
The Decca system was superseded by satellite technology. It was discontinued worldwide in 2000.

GPS satellite navigation system (GPS) are global navigation systems using satellites. Exact locations can be calculated from the satellite signals independent of weather, day or season, on land, in the air or at sea. The term GPS for the NAVSTAR-GPS of the US Department of Defense has generally been accepted. This has been fully functioning since 1995 and is also used in the civil area and in shipping today. The system has 24 satellites circling the earth at a height of approx. 20,200 km. At any time, at least three satellites equipped with atomic clocks are within range of any point on earth. The identification, position and exact time of the emission of the signal are the most important items of information sent by the satellites. The GPS receiver compares the time at which the signal was emitted with the time of its reception, the distance of the satellite being determined from the difference. The user's own position is calculated from the measurement of two more satellites. With continuous recalculation, direction of movement and speed can also be determined.

object. Initially three to four magnifications were thus considered acceptable. The Kepler telescope was no solution, because it turns images upside down. A middle way was found for the larger field of vision and stronger magnification in the 19th c. Most instruments of that time could be extended only once and were about 50 cm long when closed. With the invention of the prismatic glass, images were no longer inverted and the telescopes shortened. However, binoculars gradually ousted monocular telescopes.

Binoculars on board
Binoculars are standard equipment on every ship. Failing to use them has had fatal consequences in the history of seafaring. The watch in the crow's nest of the 'Titanic' was not provided with any of the four ship's binoculars and thus did not see the fatal iceberg until it was too late.
A set of binoculars, also called field glasses, consists of two identical or mirror-sym-.

metric telescopes configured parallel to one another. Unlike monocular telescopes, they provide a three-dimensional image, an impression of depth and the possibility of gauging distances.
Most early binoculars were designed and functioned like the Galilean telescope. Today's powerful binoculars are based on the principle of the Kepler lens telescope: prisms are installed in the beam path of the instruments to reflect and redirect the incident light beams. The image is thus not upside down as with the classic lens telescopes, but appears upright and true-to-side.

Europe is currently investing massively in the development of its own satellite navigation system 'Galileo', intended exclusively for civil purposes.

The **Echo sounder** is used for the electro-acoustic measurement of water depths and location of fish. It was invented by the German physicist Alexander Behm, who applied for a patent in 1913.

Echo sounders emit short sound or ultrasonic pulses and measure the time they need to return as echo to the ship. The echo results from the reflection of the beam on another medium or obstacle, e.g. the seabed or fish. The more exactly the speed of the noise can be registered – it alters with the temperature and density (salinity) of the water – the more precise the measurement is. The signal received as echo is given as depth reading in the unit.

Ship radar. In April 1904, the German engineer Christian Hülsmeyer applied for a patent for a 'procedure for reporting to an observer distant metallic objects via electric waves'. The idea for radar was born. The principle was then forgotten and not rediscovered until the early 1930s. Today, radar (Radio Detecting and Ranging) is used in space, on land, in the air and in and on the water. Ships use radar for locating other vessels. However, radar bearings are also useful for determining

the direction and distance of land and sea marks. Ship radar units operate as units with rotating aerials emitting electromagnetic pulses. The resulting electromagnetic waves are reflected by the objects they hit and received as pulses by the rotating aerials (echo principle). This occurs at the speed of light. The received pulses (blips) form connected to one another a presentation similar to a map on the luminescent screen of the receiving unit. The centre of the screen corresponds to the location of the operator's own aerial. A compass scale is used for taking bearings.

7 GLOBES AND NAUTICAL CHARTS

Cartography: From religious world view to conformal projection

Even in prehistoric times, men painted or scratched maps on rock walls. Among the oldest known are the wall paintings of Çatal Hüyük (Turkey, ca. 6200 BC), which depict the plan of a settlement. Even in ancient Greece, scholars like Pythagoras (ca. 570–ca. 500 BC) and Aristotle (384–322 BC) realised that the earth is a sphere and attempted to transfer sections of the curved surface of the earth on to paper. However, distortions were created with the projection. Cartographers sought a solution to this problem for 2,000 years. Practical cartography played a great role in Roman times. The Roman road maps, called 'itineraria', included details of

World map by Edward Wright, 'corrected and extended' by J. Moxon, 1655
Mathematician and astronomer Edward Wright's (1561–1615) world map, first published in 1600, represents the continents and oceans in a Mercator projection.

Highlight:
Atlantis
Majoris.
The first nauti-
cal atlas to be
published in the
Netherlands,
from the 17th
century.

Atlantis Majoris Quinta Pars, Orbem Maritimum Joannes Janssonius, Amsterdam, 1657
This windrose in six languages is part of the first nautical atlas to be printed in the Netherlands. It achieved wide distribution in the German-speaking world as 'Grosser Atlantis, welcher begreiffet die Wasser-Welt' (Great Atlantis, who Rules the Water-World).

distances and indicated the easiest routes to take.

In the Middle Ages, maps of the world were drawn to represent theological mindsets rather than the geographical reality. On most of them, Jerusalem is shown in the centre, with the continents of Asia, Africa and Europe being separated by lines in the form of a 'T'. Only in the 15th c. did the 'Geographia' of Claudius Ptolemy (ca. 100–ca. 175 AD) come as manuscript from Byzantium to Italy. This work of late antiquity was very widely circulated thanks to the advent of book printing. The invention of the conformal projection of the surface of the earth on a map in the 16th c. was the next milestone. Modern cartography began with the precise determination of longitude at the end of the 17th c.

Mercator projection. Sailors need conformal (angle-preserving) charts for precise navigation at sea. Mathematician and geographer Gerardus Mercator (1512–1594) created such a map in 1569. On his map Mercator progressively increased the distances between lines of latitude from the equator to the poles. This principle allowed navigators to connect widely dispersed destinations with straight lines: the lines always intersect the lines of longitude at the same angle. Mercator's ingenious reasoning enabled compass-guided course setting for the first time. To this day, navigators refer to conformal, angle-preserving map projections as 'Mercator projections'.

**Nieuwe Thresoor der Zee-vaert.
J. Waghenaer,** Amsterdam, 1609. The sailing handbook 'New Treasure of Navigation' contains numerous charts of coastal regions as well as coastal surveys and descriptions.

Nuevo Atlas de las Partes Orientales de Europa Joan Blaeu, Amsterdam, 1659
In the 17th century, the market for maps, globes and atlases was dominated by the Blaeu family in Amsterdam.
Willem Janszoon Blaeu had founded their company in 1596. Around 1660, when the 'New Atlas of Eastern Europe' was published, the Blaeus' company was at its peak. Nearly one million maps and cityscapes were printed with more than a thousand copper plates.

Recueil Contenant des Cartes Nouvelles
Le Rouge, Paris, 1742. The 'Collection of New Maps' was published by the cartographer and copper engraver Georges Louis Le Rouge.

Copper engraving of nautical charts
For a long time, the technique of copperplate engraving provided the most attractive nautical charts with incomparable sharpness, fineness and softness of colours. Engraving

De Fransche Neptunus of Nieuwe Atlas van de Zeekaarten
Pieter Mortier, Amsterdam, 1693. 'The Fransche Neptunus or New Atlas of Nautical Charts, Compiled and Engraved by Explicit Order of the King for use by his Navy'. The magnificent atlas is coloured by hand. Besides maps it contains detailed illustrations of ships and tables with navigation information.

a map was a time-consuming task, often taking up to a year and requiring experienced copper engravers. Various techniques can be used for producing the printing plates. With the cold needle process, the nautical chart is laterally reversed with grooves, lines and hatching mechanically etched in the copper plate, after which the plate is rubbed in with printing ink and then the surface is cleaned. The printing ink remains in the grooves, and the plate is ready for printing. The history of copperplate engraving in Europe goes back to the Early Middle Ages. The copper engraving map was used first for the 27 sheets of the Florentine edition of the Ptolemaic maps (1487) and became increasingly common from the beginning of the 17th c. The advantages were that plates could be later corrected and the nautical charts were easily legible on board and could be erased – since the invention of the eraser in 1770. Since 1960, the copper engraving lost its significance in nautical chart production.

Map of Denmark, around 1630
Chalcography. Engraved by Abraham Goos
Printing: Nicolaus Johann Piscator (Claes Janss Visscher), Amsterdam

Map of America, c. 1780
Chalcography, engraving and printing: Gebrüder Lotter, Augsburg. The 'Carte de l'Amérique' shows the routes of the three exploration and research voyages of James Cook.

Celestial globe, England, late 19th century
Manufacturer: Cary Porter Co., London, 'Makers to the Admiralty' Celestial globes with

fixed stars made it possible to answer many astronomical questions without advance calculations. It is apparent from inventory lists and instrument vendor catalogues that many ships were equipped with such globes.

Pocket globe England, 18th century
Terrestrial globe from papier-mâché in a sharkskin case. Representation of the heavens with planets on the case.

Two pocket globes: terrestrial and celestial globes England, mid-19th century
Signed: 'Newton's New & Improved Terrestrial Globe' and 'Newton's New & Improved Celestial Globe'

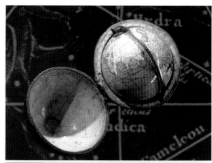

Behaim globe
(reproduction)
The so-called 'Earth apple' by Martin Behaim (1459–1507) is considered to be the oldest terrestrial globe. The original dates from 1492 – the year that Columbus discovered America. The 'New World' is therefore not shown on the globe.

Drawing instruments for nautical charts
19th–20th century
Various implements were used for the work of drafting nautical charts. Besides the divider, which could be used to transfer distances on a map, there was the compass, used to simplify complex calculations, the centimetre ruler, protractor and various rulers: universal ruler, triangle, parallel ruler.

Drawing instruments in mahogany box
England, around 1850. So-called commander drawing instruments. They were a part of privately owned navigation instruments used by naval officers.

Drawing compass in a ray-skin case
around 1780

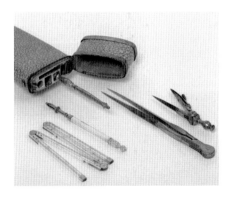

Newly founded Mathematical Work School, Nicolai Bion, Leipzig, 1713
'Or thorough instruction/ on how to use mathematical instruments not only properly and correctly/ but also to manufacture/ test/ and always maintain them in good condition/ in the best and most accurate manner'.
Includes 'The seventh book. On the preparation and use of the instruments/ which are useful for navigation'.

8 TERRESTRIAL NAVIGATION: LIGHTHOUSES, LIGHTSHIPS AND BUOYS

The earliest shipping routes were mostly along coasts, as these offered good orientation to mariners. Important landmarks were hills or groups of trees and later buildings, particularly churches. Views from the sea were recorded as 'depictions' in sea manuals.
Buoys, beacons and stone towers, which were initially all called 'beacons' ('signs'), were sited on coasts to improve orientation. Lighthouses and lightships were also used to enable seafarers to navigate safely at night as well as in the daytime.
The 'Pharos' of Alexandria, built in the 3rd c. BC and destroyed in an earthquake in the 14th c., is regarded as one of the first lighthouses. The word for 'lighthouse' (phare, faro) is derived from it in, for instance, the Romance languages. There were a few dozen lighthouses in the Mediterranean region already at the time of the Roman Empire. Parallel to the creation of ever new lighthouse buildings, improvements were made in light sources and optical instruments. Direction lights and leading lights continue to be indispensable for shipping, while long-range lights have become somewhat less significant as navigational aids.

Leading lights Leading lights comprise mostly a lower light and an upper light behind it. By orienting himself to these, a seafarer can determine his position relatively exactly. Leading lights are thus used mainly for entrances and narrow ship channels (e.g., rivers).
The vessel is exactly on course (on the 'leading light line') if you can see from it the higher light exactly behind the lower light. They are often switched synchronously so that they can be allocated to one another more easily.

180 degree Fresnel lens from a front light
Manufacturer: Pintsch,
Berlin-Fürstenwalde, 1929
The lens was used in the Wremerloch
(Außenweser) front light. Owned by the Wa-
terways and Shipping Office of Bremerhaven.

Illuminating lens of a rear light
Manufacturer: probably Picht or Weule,
before 1900. The lens was used until 1992 in
a rear light.

Roter Sand Lighthouse
Mouth of the Weser, Germany, Constructed
in 1883–1885, Construction material: iron
plates, Height 28 m above high water mark.
For more than three quarters of a century,
the Roter Sand ('Red Sand') Lighthouse was
the dominant lighthouse for navigation into
the Weser river. It was permanently shut
down in 1986. Since 1987, the lighthouse has
been owned by the German Foundation for
Monument Protection. During the waves of
emigration starting in 1885, the Roter Sand
lighthouse was the last glimpse that many
Germans had of their homeland. This and its
characteristic design made it a symbol for
lighthouses in Germany. Model maker: Günter
Strepp and Hans Helge Staack

Faro de Punta del Hidalgo
East Tenerife, Spain, Constructed in 1991–92
Construction material: concrete, height 50 m
This lighthouse is an example of modern
navigational aid design that seeks harmony with nature and its environment. The
design of the lighthouse suggests an arch
pointing out to sea, constructed using a
type of crystal found in the volcanic rock
of the island. The architect intended to
make a special impression through harmony
with the ancient rocks of Tenerife. In the
lighthouse's lamp there is a rotating lens
assembly with three lights. Model maker:
Günter Strepp

Buoy tender 'Mellum'
The buoy tender 'Mellum' was built in 1935
at Flender shipyard, Lübeck, for the Navigation Marks and Maritime Pilot Office of
the Jade. 1:50 scale, Model maker: Günther
Schmidt

Lightship
'Bürgermeister O'Swald'/'Elbe 1'
Built at the Meyer shipyard in Papenburg
for the Waterways Office in Cuxhaven, the
legendary lightship was put into service in
1948. Identifier: 10 seconds at regular intervals (5 sec. bright/5 sec. dark). The 'Bürgermeister O'Swald' was manned for 40 years
as a navigational mark at the mouth of the
Elbe river (station Elbe 1). Decommissioned
in 1988 it became a museum ship at
Cuxhaven in 1990. Scale: 1:100

9 **LEGO SHIP 'QUEEN MARY 2' ('QM2')** Model built of approx. 780,000 LEGO bricks, length: 690 cm, width: 82 cm, height 144 cm, weight: c. 870 kg, time for construction: c. 1,200 hours, Jan. until June 2008, builder (shipyard and service equipment): Klaas H. Meyaard, builder (ship): Rene' Hoffmeister. The blocks were not sponsored by LEGO. The passenger ship 'Queen Mary II', operated by the British shipping company Cunard, was built in France by Chantiers de l'Atlantique, Saint-Nazaire, and was launched in 2004.

With a length of 345 metres, the 'QM2' is one of the largest passenger ships in the world. It has capacity for up to 2,620 passengers and has a crew of 1,253.

Kugelbake navigation mark

The Kugelbake ('Ball Beacon') is a former navigation mark that was used for the approach to Cuxhaven. It is the symbol of the City.

The first Kugelbake was probably built in 1703. Since the structure is made of wood, its lifetime was never very long. Every 30 years (at the most), the navigation mark had to be replaced or restored. From 1853 to 1878, the Kugelbake served as a lighthouse. By 2001, it had lost its nautical importance. Since 2002, the Kugelbake has been owned by the city of Cuxhaven and is protected as a historical landmark. The current design dates back to 1945. Scale approx. 1:100

10 **NAVIGATION IN THE SHIP SIMULATOR**

Take the helm on the bridge of the 'Tokyo Express'! The Ship Simulator on Deck 1 allows visitors to experience the ports of Rotterdam, Singapore and Hamburg on board a container vessel. Under the expert supervision of our captains, you can navigate a c. 300 m long container ship through various scenarios. Public voyages are held regularly. The cost of participation is included in the entrance fee, and no reservation is necessary. Additional information can be found on the Museum's website.

Highlight:
Ship simulator
Ship steering for everyone – in a simulator.

HIGHLIGHTS ON DECK 2

Cordage workshop: Here one can see how ropes are being made or how a cable is protected against chafing.

Book shaped display cases: six chapters of maritime history in specially designed showcases.

Model of the galleon 'Bull' (1546): Race build English galleons like this one contributed to the success against the Spanish Armada.

Diorama 'Der Aufbruch' ('The Departure'): Dutch ships put to sea off Texel, a few days later they would engage in the famous Four Days Battle against an English fleet.

Oil painting 'Ostindienfahrer vor einem Hafen' (East Indiamen off a harbour): trade with India and the Far East brought power and wealth to European trading companies, since the 17th century.

Silver bars with VOC (Dutch East India Company) stamp. Precious metals were a welcome currency in Asian trade.

English ships medical chest: this chest, still holding its original contents, bears testament to a time when scurvy and yellow fever lost their terrors.

Gun deck from a British corvette: bronze cannons, swords, swivel guns. Here one can see what was needed

for a naval battle in the days of Admiral Nelson.

Model of the galleon 'Golden Hind' (1577): with this ship, the privateer Francis Drake sailed against the Spaniards in the Pacific. The model won a Naviga bronze medal.

Model of the fivemast full-rigged ship 'Preußen' (1902): this ship was considered to represent technical perfection among sailing ships.

Painting 'Sail Training Ship Deutschland' (1927): Painter Adolf Bock creates the impression of a ghost ship approaching through the fog.

WITH THE WIND AROUND THE WORLD: SAILING SHIPS

The exhibits on Deck 2 present the Age of Sail. For millennia, the forces of nature – currents, weather and especially the wind – have determined how fast a ship could reach its destination. Viking ships, vessels from the Hanseatic League, Galleons, Frigates and Ships of the Line from the great maritime powers as well as the Tall Ships (Windjammers) which were the last big commercially used sailing ships all can be found here. A separate part of the deck is devoted to pirates, who terrorize the high seas even today.

A 3.5-metre-long model of the 'Wapen von Hamburg III' hangs proudly in the atrium. The 52-gun ship was launched in 1722. Its mission was to accompany ship convoys from Hamburg to the Mediterranean. A group of merchants at the time financed warships that were meant to defend Hamburg's trade ships against pirate attacks. The 'Wapen von Hamburg III' sailed under the coat of arms of the citys admiralty until 1737. Following its sale, it was converted into a cargo ship. Scale: 1:14, Model maker: Eduard Willke

1 SEAFARING IN ANCIENT TIMES

Mariners have used the wind to propel their vessels for thousands of years. The sailors of antiquity were skilled seafarers. By the 2nd millennium BC, the Minoans put out to sea from Crete. They reached nearly all harbours in the eastern Mediterranean and maintained a prosperous overseas trade. Later, the Phoenicians and Greeks did the same. Both maritime nations established colonies and trading outposts throughout the Mediterranean and beyond. Finally, Rome was able to completely dominate the Mediterranean for a few centuries.

2 POLYNESIANS

Already a few centuries before Christ, Polynesian boat designers constructed double-hulled sailing canoes. With these, they managed to travel thousands of kilometres at sea. Due to the special design, the canoes were less prone to rolling in the wind than boats with only one hull. Navigation and discoveries were made through

Waa Kaulua Model of a long distance-capable double-hulled canoe by the model maker Lothar Finger. Vessels such as these made settlement of the Polynesian Triangle possible, and connected the widely scattered archipelagos.

observation of the sea, sky and stars. The Polynesians also had nautical charts made from sticks and mussels.

Model of a stick chart
Stick charts were Polynesian navigational instruments made from coconut leaf ribs and coconut fibres. Cowry shells marked islands, bent sticks showed currents and straight sticks showed the various directions of travel.

Egyptian ships
By the time of the Old Kingdom (c. 2,700–2,200 BC), the Egyptians had a merchant fleet and a navy. They sailed mainly to Lebanon to trade cedar, but also to the legendary land of Punt, rich with gold, believed to be in eastern Africa. On the relief, a shipload of cattle is pictures with a plank beneath as a gangway. Next to this there is a group of gesticulating sailors.

Replica: plaster replica workshop of the Prussian Cultural Heritage Foundation. Original: limestone; New Kingdom, 18th dynasty, 14th century BC, Egyptian Museum Berlin

Trireme (Athens, c. 400 BC)
Around 650 BC, the best-known ancient ship type appeared, probably in Corinth: the trireme. It was a versatile speedboat about 40 m in length, with a combination of the propulsion systems known at the time: three rows of oars and a square sail as auxiliary power. Triremes were built to be light so that they were well-suited for battles at sea. They were less suitable for sailing on the high seas. Construction and maintenance could only be afforded by wealthy city-states. Scale: 1:50, Model maker: Erwin Scherer

Trireme

Sail types
Representations
of the most com-
mon sail types.

DECK 2

39

Square sail

The square sail is the oldest known sail. The Egyptians and Phoenecians used it as well as the Vikings. It has the shape of a rectangle or a trapezoid and is attached to a 'yard'. The yard is a horizontal bar (typically a log), hoisted in the middle of the mast. This way the sail stays at right angles to the ship. The square sail requires the wind to blow if at all possible in the direction of the intended course (diagonally from aft).

Lateen sail

The lateen seil was known in Arab lands by the 1st century AD. By the 8th century it was the most widely used rig in the Mediterranean. It typically has a triangular shape, sometimes also slightly trapezoidal and is set on an oblique 'yard'. The yard is nearly double the length of the mast. The lateen sail can be longer than the ship itself. It was the first 'fore-and-aft sail' – a sail normally positioned lenghtwise to the ship.

Lugsail

The origin of the lugsail is not known. It has the shape of a quadrangular fore-and-aft sail, set lenghtwise to the ship on a rather steeply angled spar, which for its part is offset sideways, loosely attached on the mast and much shorter than that for the lateen sail. The lugsail only requires a single line for hoisting. It mostly proved useful on ship's boats (utility boats). It is easy to handle as when tacking it can be shifted around the mast without the sail first having to be taken in.

Gaff sail

The gaff sail was invented by the Dutch and became common from the 17th c. It has an irregular rectangular shape. The name comes from the gaff, a spar that is forked-shaped on the lower end and holds the mast like a "claw". The sail is tautened between the boom (which also clasps the mast and remains below) and the gaff by pulling the gaff diagonally upwards. The gaff sail was far superior to all other sails of its time. It was one of the most effective sails up into the last century..

Staysail

A stay is a wire rope or a massive steel pole that holds the mast lenghtwise to the ship either forward or aft (standing backstay) to prop it up or brace it ("stay" meaning to hold taut, etc.) Stays can also connect the tops of the masts with one another. A staysail is a triangular sail attached on a stay with jib hanks, which are hooks that have to be weatherproof, simple to open and easily accessible. Thus a staysail can be hoisted easily with a rope (halyard).

3 SEAFARING IN THE MIDDLE AGES

THE VIKINGS

The Vikings are without doubt among the most impressive seafarers of the Middle Ages. Wherever the Norsemen landed, they acted as traders and warriors. From their homelands in the north of Europe, they sailed to Iceland and Greenland, where they permanently settled. In the year 1001, the explorer Leif Eriksson (979–1020) even managed to land in America from there. For their voyages, Scandinavian sailors used clinker-planked ships suited to the high seas: technical feats unequalled in their day in Europe. Sidenote: the term 'Viking' is misleading. It does not describe a people, but rather the activities of a seafaring warrior.

Viking longship (Norway, 9th century) The Vikings created an advanced maritime culture. Ships such as the one shown could sail at up to 12 knots. This model, built by Ingo Drössler, is modelled according to a shipwreck found at Oseberg (Norway). Scale: 1:35

Viking merchant ship
(c. 1000 AD). The Viking merchant ship was called a knarr. The model shown here is based on the discoveries at Gokstad in Norway (1880) and Skuldelev in Denmark (1963). The ships had a wider and rounder shape than the Oseberg ship, and their speed and manoeuvrability was inferior to that of the longships. Knarrs were cargo sailing ships used to transport goods at sea. Scale: 1:35, Model maker: Casa dos Descobertas, U. Porath/ M. Porath

Picture stone from Lärbro Tängelgärda I,
(8th century, original: open-air museum at Bunge, Gotland)
In the upper left, two warriors cross their swords in an oath. The context is the death of two men. Alongside the crime is pictured: a man was murdered with a dagger, and the second victim is already lying dead under his horse. In the row of images below, three men wait with lowered swords. The god Odin rides on to the scene on his eight-legged stallion Sleipnir. The third row of images shows how the slain rider is carried to Valhalla.

Viking
sword

Viking longship

THE HANSEATIC LEAGUE

Since the 12th century there have been merchant guilds in Europe who did business under the name Hanse. This confederation was created to protect merchants on trade journeys and to represent mutual economic interests abroad. Soon the cities became suitable protectors of the trade routes. Rich merchants made their way into the highest political positions in the cities, and thus the interests of the cities and the merchants became intertwined. Agreements and alliances were made. This made the Hanseatic League of Merchants into the Hanseatic League of Cities, which was in full bloom in the 14th century. A closely connected network of 30 larger and about 200 smaller cities between Cologne and Reval (now Tallinn, Estonia) was formed, with large offices in London, Bruges, Bergen and Novgorod. The first joint 'Hansetag' (Hanseatic Congress) took place in 1356, while the last meeting was held in 1669. The Hanseatic League was never formally dissolved.

Seal with cog ship from the city of Elbing (casting)

Hanseatic cog (ship), around 1350, based on the seal of the city of Elbing. The Hanseatic cog was an improvement on a Frisian coastal vessel. As the Hanseatic League emerged, this ship design spread to the Baltic Sea, where local variations were also produced. Large cogs in the Late Middle Ages carried up to 200 tonnes of cargo and represented the most important technical asset of the Hanseatic league. A stern rudder translated the power of the wind (caught in a square sail) optimally onto the course of the ship. Scale: 1:50, Model maker: Ingo Drössler

Nef (ship) from Winchelsea, England, c 1250. Nefs were the name for cog-like ships on the west coast of France. It repre-sented a hybrid between a Viking merchant ship and the more voluminous ship types of the romanic tradition. The widespread use of the nef is evidenced by visual represen-tations of them on city seals throughout northern and western Europe, as well as models from Spain and Portugal.
Scale: 1:50, Model maker: Ingo Drössler

Carrack The model shows a carvel-planked ship from the city of Lübeck. Until the Late Middle Ages, the so-called clinker method of boat building was common: planks were laid in an overlapping manner, and supporting ribs stabilized the resulting shell. The Portuguese term 'caravela' then arrived in the north via Hanseatic trade routes. It described a new ship type and became a synonym for a new shipbuilding technique. The frame construc-tion and edge-to-edge arrangement of the planks made larger ship hulls possible. Terms like "caravela", "caravel" or "caravel-built" evolved into the german terms "Kraweel" and "Kraweelbauweise". The technique came from the Med-iterranean region and was already known to the ancient Egyptians. The first appearance of a large carvel-built ship in the Baltic Sea

Carrack

led to a quick transition from clinker building to carvel building, starting in 1462.
Scale: 1:50, Model maker: unknown

4 CORDAGE WORKSHOP CORDAGE DEVELOPMENT

One of the most basic tools of mankind was and continues to be the rope. Even Neanderthals had simple binding materials. Weapons, tools and boats were inconceivable without such tools. The first rope finds made of papyrus and esparto grass came from Upper Egypt (c. 5,000 BC). The first hemp ropes were twisted around 2800 BC in China.

Techniques

The classic method for making a rope is by twisting. First, fibres are spun together into yarns, and then these are twisted into strands. Several strands are twisted into ropes. Another step is twisting into a hawser from three or four ropes.

> **Highlight: Cordage workshop.**
> Here one can see amongst other things how ropes are being made or how a cable is protected against chafing.

Another method of manufacturing a rope is braiding. The number of fibre bundles varies in this method. The higher the number, the less round the rope is and the more tube-like it is. Braided ropes are usually softer and more elastic than twisted ropes.

Materials

This collection shows a wide range of materials used for the manufacture of cordage, including hemp, sisal (from a species of agave native to Mexico), coconuts, manila hemp (from the stem of a banana species) and cotton. Before the invention of synthetic fibres, cotton ropes were commonly used as sheet ropes (lines for setting a sail), since they had a very soft grip.

Polypropylene makes for a buoyant rope with low elongation and good UV resistance.

Polyethylene (PE) gives a non-buoyant rope with low elongation and high UV stability. Usable up to 225°C.

Aramid (Kevlar) is a non-buoyant fibre with very low elongation and poor UV stability. An aramid rope takes in up to 70 per cent water. It is not abrasion resistant, but it may be used up to 400°C.

The first archaeological evidence for a **cable rope** comes from Pompeii. In the ruins of the city, which was buried in 79 AD by an eruption of Mount Vesuvius, a three-metre-long three-strand bronze cable was found. The first cordage made from steel wire was manufactured in 1834 by 'Oberbergrat' (mining supervisor) Wilhelm August Julius Albert in Clausthal for mining applications. In 1835 a patent for its use in ships was filed in England by Andrew Smith.

Since the twentieth century, synthetic fibres have been developed for rope production. Because of their favourable qualities and durability, they have largely superseded natural fibres. The availability of a wide variety of materials and production methods enable highly specialized cordage construction for a wide variety of applications. High-quality synthetic line now even serves as an alternative to steel cables and chains. The collection also shows special tools used in sail- and cordage making.

In the cordage workshop

Fife rail with belaying pins and cleanly coiled cordage. Order is half of life, even at sea.

Reeperbahn (Ropewalk) Cordage is made here. A reeperbahn is a workshop for this process. Here, ropes are made into hawsers (thick ropes for mooring and towing). Since ropes are usually very long, ropewalks had a lenght of up to 400 m. The ropemaker had to lay the long strands along the ropewalk before he could twist or braid them into rope.

The origin of sailor's knots
Seafaring people worked out useful sailor's knots early on. Without them, the operation of boats and ships was not possible. Sailor's knots had to be practical and quickly tied. It must also be possible for them to be quickly untied, even in wet conditions or under heavy loads. Ordinary knots are incapable of this. They significantly reduce the breaking load of a line or hawser.
Artefacts from the Palaeolithic (flint axes, spearheads) suggest that people were already aware of binding materials such as animal sinews many thousands of years ago, and that they knew simple knots. Remains of Stone Age nets have been preserved in bogs and deserts. The clothing and possessions of the 5,300-year-old glacier mummy 'Ötzi' show examples of simple hitches, overhand knots and a reef knot. The Greek physician Heraklas described 18 orthopaedic slings in the 1st century AD, which were published in the 4th century by Oribasius of Pergamom in his medical encyclopaedia. Among these knots were the reef knot and the clove hitch.

Individual knots
Bowline The simple bowline is used to form a fixed loop that does not tighten on itself on the end of a line or hawser. A loop such as this is used to secure a line to a dolphin or a bollard.

Clove hitch Used to secure the end of a line to an object, bollard or dolphin.

Reef knot Used to attach two lines of equal strength. Used especially for reef lines and seizings.

Sheet bend Used to connect two lines of unequal strength.

5.1 TRADE AND POWER: CHINA
Fearing for his own life, Emperor Qin Shihuangdi (259 BC–290 BC) sent a few thousand young Chinese on an expedition to search for the elixir of life on the fabled Island of the Immortals. The departure of this fleet is documented (as well as another fleet two years later), but they never returned and are said to have landed in Japan. The expedition demonstrates the early advent of sea navigation along the Yellow Sea coast. In the first century, some Chinese knew permanent routes in the South China Sea and in the eastern Indian Ocean. By the turn of the 6th century, Chinese ships appeared west of India. As Arabs came to dominate the Indian Ocean, maritime trade to and from China picked up. In order to promote this, Arabian merchants set up their own trading outposts in India, Ceylon, Malaysia, Sumatra and in a few cities in

southern China. Trade activities increased yet more during the following centuries and reached their peak in the 14th century. The city of Quanzhou became an economic and cultural centre for maritime trade with India and the Arab world. Its harbour was one of the most important in the world, and it counted even Marco Polo among its visitors. The Chinese Zheng He (1371–1433 or 1435) undertook a total of seven sea voyages to India, into the Persian Gulf and to Africa between 1405 and 1433. These were the first major sea voyages by the Chinese into regions, which had already been explored and dominated be Arabian, Indian and Persian seafarers.

Chinese treasure ship, around 1405
The model was built in China for the International Maritime Museum Hamburg with the donations of the Chinese community in Hamburg. The historical examples are nine-mast treasure ships, claimed to have been over 120 metres long and 50 metres in beam. These historical references are however in doubt among modern researchers. It is undisputed that the hull of these ships was criss-crossed with watertight transverse bulkheads, a technique that only took hold in Europe in the 19th century. The treasure ships were the flagships of the large fleet of Admiral Zheng He.

Zhang Zeduan 'Qingming shanghe tu'
Zhang Zeduan was a painter in the Northern Song Dynasty (960–1127). The roll shows everyday life in the capital Kaifeng on Qingming, the Chinese day of remembrance for the dead. In the canals there are passenger and merchant ships as well as a boatyard. The painting is the artist's most famous and has frequently been copied and reinterpreted. This copy shows the original version.

Tableware, China, 10th century
This porcelain is of Chinese origin and comes from the hold of a ship which sunk in about 960 AD. It was salvaged in 1997 together with c. 12,000 other precious items 150 miles northwest of Jakarta at 26 metres depth.

5.2 TRADE AND POWER: THE SEA ROUTE TO INDIA / SPAIN AND PORTUGAL

The age of seafarers and explorers in Europe began in the 15th century. The motivation behind their voyages was the search for a maritime route to India (see also Deck 1: 'The age of the famous discoverers' with maps of their voyages).
The demand for exotic goods like spices as well as the hunger for precious metals was tremendous in Europe, and so was the competition with the rich Arabian middlemen who had controlled the market until that time. High duties that the Ottoman Empire and Venice charged on goods drove prices up. As a result, Spanish and Portuguese captains searched for a maritime trade route to India on behalf of their monarchs. With the special support of a son of the Portuguese king, Henry the Navigator (1394–1460), exploration of the west coast of Africa began in 1418.
Starting in 1433, Henry began to gather scholars and sailors at his residence in Sagres (Algarve), who compiled current nautical knowledge and made it available for new expeditions. Around 1488, Bartolomeu Diaz (1450–1500) was the first to round the Cape of Good Hope, thus paving the way to India. Vasco da Gama (1469–1524) completed this mission in 1498 by landing at Kozhikode (Calicut) in southern India. Trade agreements were reached and outposts were created in the Indian Ocean. In this manner, Portugal bypassed the old overland 'spice route'. In the Battle of Diu of 1509, 18 Portuguese ships prevailed over 100 dhows and galleys of a fleet sent against them by a coalition of Egypto-Arabian and Indian rulers and that was cofinanced by Venice and the Ottomans. They all feared losing their profits in the spice trade. With the victory, the foundation was laid for the naval dominance of Portugal in the western Indian Ocean.
In 1492, the Genoese Christopher Columbus set sail toward the west on behalf of Spain. He accepted that Earth was spherical and hoped to reach India by going west. As is

well known, he instead landed in America. In the European Age of Discovery, a competition for trading posts, sea routes and colonies began. In order to prevent a war between the Catholic maritime powers Spain and Portugal, the Treaty of Tordesillas was signed on 7 July 1494 by decree of Pope Alexander VI. He declared that all land west of a particular north-to-south line through the Atlantic would be granted to Spain, and that all land to the east would go to Portugal. This gave Portugal control over the still undiscovered sea route to India, while Spain could conquer its colonial empire in the Americas. Another dividing line was agreed upon on in 1529 defining the interests of both powers in the Pacific. Other European states did not accept these treaties and soon they as well forcibly entered the maritime trade. In 1522 the French privateer Jean Fleury took a gold shipment (that had been previously looted by Hernán Cortés in Mexico) from the Spanish at the Azores. When the Spanish king Charles V demanded back his 'possession', the French king Francis I is reputed to have replied that he would be glad to see the passage in Adam's testament that made Spain and Portugal the sole heirs to the new lands. Until then, he'd rather keep the gold for himself.

Caravel, Portugal c. 1500

Caravels were one of the most important Mediterranean ship types with lateen sails. Predecessors to this ship type were already in use sincee in the mid-13th century off the coast of Portugal as cargo and fishing vessels. Today, caravels are among the best-known ship types in maritime history: from the mid-15th century, they were used by explorers who set out to discover new lands. They opened up the sea routes to India and the New World for Spain and Portugal. Scale 1:50,
Model maker: Ingo Drössler

Galley 'Fulmen in Hostes'

In the naval battles with the Ottomans, the galley was the most common warship for centuries. It was typically rowed by convicts and prisoners of war, but volunteers also took part. Unlike pure sailing warships, they could only carry guns in the bow and stern. Model based on Josef Furttenbach (1591–1667). His 'Architectura Navalis' was published in around 1629 and was the first German-language book on ship building. Scale: 1:50, Model maker: G. Schiwek.

Caravel

Portuguese cannons, 16th cent.
The forged barrels, also called 'lombarda' in Spanish, were salvaged in 1962 from the wreckage of a Portuguese East Indiamen off the coast of Madagascar. The barrels mounted on wooden stands were breechloaders with a separate powder chamber (chambers missing here), which were blocked against the barrel with a wooden wedge. With calibres of 10 and 13 cm, even cannonballs of stone were shot out of these guns.

> **Highlight:**
> **Book shaped display cases:** six chapters of maritime history in specially designed showcases.

5.3 TRADE AND POWER: THE OTTOMANS

Ottoman naval powers

When the turks arrived in Anatolia during the 10th century they begant to adopt seafaring from coastal inhabitants, starting in the 11th century. Since the Turks were mounted warriors, it was still a long time before they recognized the importance of warships. At first, they only used ships as troop transporters. After the conquest of Constantinople Sultan Mehmet II (1430–1481) was the first to have a powerfull navy built. Selim I (1470–1520) invested substantial financial resources to further expand the fleet. In the mid-16th century, the Ottomans dominated the eastern Mediterranean. An outstanding figure from the era was Hayreddin Barbarossa (1475–1546), who ascended from being a pirate captain to being commander-in-chief of the Ottoman fleet. With the conquest of Algiers, he had established his own base of operations. Under pressure from Christian naval powers, Hayreddin had to ask for assistance from the Sultan, resulting in Algiers being subject to the Ottoman Empire in 1516. In August 1538 Barbarossa defeated the Venetian navy and the so-called Holy League in the Battle of Preveza. After this triumph, the Ottoman fleet initially enjoyed the reputation of invincibility.

Lepanto

In 1571 Sultan Selim II (1524–1574) challenged the christian powers by seizing Cyprus, which at the time belonged to Venice. The Venetians managed to reassemble the Holy League and organize a powerful naval campaign. The last and greatest galley battle in history ended on 7 October 1571 with the crushing defeat of the Ottoman fleet at Lepanto. The Christian alliance fought united under the command of John of Austria. Its fleet possessed a superior firepower due to the deployment of Galeasses, an advanced version of the galley that could fire broadsides while the conventional galley only carried guns in its bow and stern. Also a Galeass was more difficult to board because her ship's side were significantly higher. Thus the galeasses proved their supremacy against the turkish fleet. After Lepanto however, the Holy League disassembled again and failled to take advantage of its victory. Already in the summer of 1572, the Ottomans again had a new fleet, though its ships were of lesser quality than the previous ones. On the one hand there was a lack of experienced crews due to the tremendous losses suffered at Lepanto and on the other hand the timber used for the ships was less well aged. In the decades that followed the Ottomans held on to the outdated galley types, a mistake that granted their christian opponents a gradual advantage.

The Naval Battle at Foca This extract from an engraving by Matthäus Merian the Younger (1621–87) shows the battle of 12 May 1649. (extract) 19 Venetian galleons triumph over 90 Turkish galleys. The advantage of the broadside-firing pure sailing ships prevailed thus ending the era of the rowed galleys as warships.

Letter by Andrea Doria

The Genoese Admiral Andrea Doria (1466–1560) was an admiral in Charles V's navy. In this letter, he reports to his monarch the conquest of Patras and a nearby castle from the turks.

Letter from Oliver Cromwell

In this letter dating from 19 February 1656 Cromwell (1599–1658) issues orders to fight the Spanish fleet at Cape Finisterre

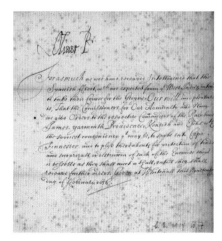

5.4 TRADE AND POWER: ENGLAND

Trade with Asia and the exploitation of colonies in the New World promised power and wealth to the European states. New maritime and trade powers quickly arose which openly challenged the supremacy of the Iberians. In the struggle with Spain, they also initially resorted to piracy. Equipped with royal letters of marque, privateers such as Francis Drake were able to take enormous riches from Spanish ships. This contributed to Philip II of Spain sending his navy, the Armada, out against England at the beginning of 1588. Owing to more modern ships and more long range artillery, England managed to fight the Armada back. The aura of her invincibility was broken. Still, the Spaniards remained a strong opponent. The attempt of England to finally shut out Spain by attacking with a counter-armada failed a year later.

Fighting and Sailing Instructions Admirals Robert Blake (1598–1657), Richard Deane (1610–1653) and George Monck (1608–1670) published two catalogues of instructions on 29 March 1653. Among other things, the naval tactic of the battle line was first described in theory. With this tactic, England was able to achieve notable victories during the First Anglo-Dutch War (1652–54).

Galleon 'Bull', England 1546

The Bull was rebuilt into a race-built galleon in 1569–70 according to the designs of Mathew Baker. It was the fastest and most manoeuvrable ship of the English navy. In the Battle of the Armada, it belonged to the squadron of Lord Admiral Effingham. Unlike the Spanish galleons, the English galleons had a greater length-to-width ratio. They were thus faster and more nimble. Scale: 1:48 Model maker: Wolfram zu Mondfeld

5.5 TRADE AND POWER: THE NETHERLANDS

In the 17th century, a new power arose in northern Europe: The Netherlands. In order to tap new sources of income, Dutch explorers followed the routes of the Portuguese around the Cape of Good Hope, and founded trading outposts in Asia. The maritime trade of exotic goods became increasingly important during this period. They quickly ousted the Portuguese from their historical territory and became the leading trade nation in Europe. Wealth and power brought the young republic into competition with England. In the 17th century, there were three naval wars between the rivals (1652–1654, 1665–1667, 1672–1674), which the tiny Netherlands survived militarily.The eventual rise of England to become the most powerful naval and trade

Highlight: Model of the 'Bull' galleon (1546): Race built english galleons like this one contributet to the success against the Spanisch Armada.

Highlight:
Diorama 'Der
Aufbruch' ('The
Departure')
Dutch ships put
to sea off Texel.
A few days later
they would
engage in the
famous four day
battle against an
English fleet

power could not be stopped in the long term by the Dutch. When the Dutchman William III of Orange was proclaimed the King of England, the rivals united, and the rise of England to become a world power began.

'Der Aufbruch' ('The Departure')

The diorama shows part of the Dutch navy departing the island of Texel. In May 1666 a Dutch fleet gathered under the command of Admiral Michiel de Ruyter (1607–76) at the anchorage off Texel. Just before they left, the Prince of Orange arrived, inspected the ships and held a naval parade. This resulted in a departure that was three days later than planned. This in turn caused the originally planned interception of the English fleet at the mouth of the

Thames to fail. In bad weather, the fleet soon anchored off Dunkirk and awaited French support. The English Admiral George Monk learned about the presence of the Dutch and promptly attacked. On 11 June 1666 his attack unleashed a huge battle, which England had to abandon on the fourth day, because it had exhausted almost all of its ammunition The battle came to be known in history as the Four Days' Battle. Scale: 1:1,250, Model maker: Roland Klinger

Letter from Cornelis Evertsen

On 26 July 1665, Admiral Cornelis Evertsen (1610–1666) informs Raads Pensionaris Huybert van Zeeland on the movements of the English fleet. The background is an attempt to bring a Dutch return fleet under

Battle of Scheveningen Engraving by Matthäus Merian the Younger (1621–87). The battle on 10 August 1653 is shown. The Dutch suffered a defeat against the English fleet under Admiral George Monck (1608–70).

Captain Pieter de Bitter (1620–1666) safely home. This led to the Battle of Vågen, in which de Bitter had to defend his convoy against an English attack. When Admiral Michiel de Ruyter finally arrived, he was able to safely escort the convoy back to the Netherlands.

Captain's letter: Gilles Schej (1644–1703) was promoted to Captain by the Admiralty of Amsterdam with this certificate.

5.6 TRADE AND POWER: THE COLONIES

With the discovery of America and the sea routes to the East, the Age of Colonialism also began. European powers expanded to other continents. Their maritime trade created the basis for the development of a global economy.

Powerful trading companies were founded, and governments granted them far-reaching privileges. They held exclusive trading rights and were allowed to independently declare and wage war.

For indigenous peoples, colonization often had catastrophic consequences. Entire peoples and cultures collapsed. In America,

millions of natives died from adventive diseases. With the conquest of the American colonies, the need for cheap labour grew. To compensate for the massive death toll among the Native Americans, colonists soon imported African slaves. The number of people trafficked from Africa grew rapidly and in the 18th century amounted to an estimated 74,000 per year. The slave trade brought advantages to the expanding economy of Europe and its colonies in the New World: it supplied plantations and mines with cheap labour, brought gold, silver and exotic goods to the great cities of Europe, meanwhile securing profitable foreign markets for domestic manufactured goods. In order to extract the greatest possible profits from the human 'goods', slave ship owners increased their transport capacity. The slaves were packed in crammed steerages that were sometimes additionally incorporated and forced to lay or crouch below deck. The transport conditions on the multi-week voyages were tough, and the mortality rate was high.

Slave chains
During transport on slave ships, Africans were secured by leg irons like these and connected to each other with additional long chains.

Alluring India
Before the invention of photography, it was common to have an illustrator on board sailing ships to artistically sketch foreign coasts, people, exotic plants and animals. The sheets shown here came from an English logbook. They show Indian cities under the control of various European colonial powers: British-controlled Madras, Danish-occupied Trankebar, Negapatam under the Dutch and Pondicherry under French occupation.
Source: Northesk Collection of Naval Papers; the drawings date from 1746.

Frigate 'Friedrich Wilhelm zu Pferde', Brandenburg, 1681
The fleet of the Great Elector was financed by letters of marque against Sweden and business on the Gold Coast of Africa. The 'Friedrich Wilhelm zu Pferde' was built in 1680–81 in Pillau. In July 1692 the ship sailed for the Brandenburg African Company to West Africa to load slaves destined for St. Thomas (Caribbean). On the return voyage, on 31 October 1693, it was captured by French warships. Scale: 1:40

East Indiamen

The oil painting by Joseph Vernet (1714–1789) shows East Indiamen off a port. Generally, any merchant ship engaged in trade with Asia was called an 'East Indiaman'. A special ship in this category was the large, heavily armed Dutch pinnace, which later led to the transom return ship, named for its notably large transom (the surface at the stern of the ship).

Silver bars with Dutch East India Company (VOC) stamp This silver is from the wreckage of the Dutch trading ship Bredenhof, which sank southeast of Africa on 6 June 1753. VOC is the abbreviation for the United Dutch East India Company (Vereenigde Oostindische Compagnie).

Chinese porcelain The porcelain comes from the wreckage of the junk Tek Sing. The ship sank on 5 February 1822 on the journey from Amoy to Batavia. The cargo was intended for the European market.

Wine bottles

These wine bottles came from the wreckage of the Dutch return ship 't'Vliegent Hart', which sank at the mouth of the Scheldt river on 3 February 1735.

6 LIFE ON BOARD OLD SAILING SHIPS

Life on sailing ships was extremely hard. The vessels were overcrowded and were often at sea for many months. Large Ships of the Line had crews of up to 950 men and more. The decks were rarely cleaned and during bad weather periods all dirt was simply washed into the bilge, the lowest compartment on the ship. For ventilation of the lower decks, the gun ports were opened. Water constantly seeped through the wooden hull, meaning that it always had to be bailed out. Moisture, darkness and bad air afflicted sailors. Seamen did incredibly difficult work, and exhaustion increased the risk of accidents. Iron-fisted discipline was required on board. Even small offences resulted in severe physical punishment. Food on long voyages was almost inedible. Drying and salting were the only ways to conserve food. For this reason, preserved food such as cured meat, stockfish (usually cod), pulses (legumes) and sea biscuits (rusks) was the norm. There was no fresh food. In addition, after a few weeks at sea, the drinking water became foul. Seamen were given a quarter litre of spirits per day to lengthen the water rations.

The mortality rate due to diseases among the crews was enormous. Particularly high losses occurred in the yellow fever regions. The greatest scourge of seafaring was scurvy, caused by vitamin C deficiency.

Highlight:
English ship's medical chest. The chest, still holding its original contents bears testament to a time when scurvy and yellow fever lost their terrors.

Only in the mid-18th century when the Scottish physician James Lind showed that the consumption of citrus fruits could prevent the outbreak of scurvy did the illness gradually lose its terror. Still, his study long went unrecognized. In the year 1810, 50 per cent of all deaths in the Royal Navy were due to illnesses, 31.5 percent were due to accidents or punishments, 10.2 percent due to shipwreck and only 8.3 percent resulted from battles.

Logbook of the 'Duchess of Athol'
This ship of the British East India Company travelled between 18 November 1829 and 16 March 1831 from London to Bombay and then onward to China. The entries on 1 May 1830 report on the court martial of the seaman Peter Quin for rebellious behaviour. He was ordered to receive four dozen lashes.

Cat-o'-Nine-Tails
Punishments were administered on English ships with such whips until well into the 19th century. Manufacturer: Karl Bareuther

Ship medical chest, England, c. 1820
In the 19th century, rules were decreed which determined which medicines were to be kept on board. Before that, this was determined by the ship-owners. Of course, there was often disagreement between the ship physician and the captain over sick leave among the crew. This ship medical chest was donated to the Museum by Prof Norbert M Meenen. It is an extremely

rare piece, since it still has its original contents. The last verifiable stock date is 1889. As such medical chests began to be carried on large ships, the old scourges of seafaring, such as scurvy, yellow fever and gangrene gradually lost their grip.

Smoking tobacco
Preserved smoking tobacco was always highly valued by seamen of all nations. If they were unable to smoke on sea voyages lasting for months, the small world of the seaman was no longer as it should be. A good supply was always brought on voyages. Temperature changes, wetness and moisture made certain measures necessary to keep tobacco flavourful and fresh over longer periods of time. One method of preservation was to wet entire dried tobacco leaves, sprinkle them with rum, wrap them in a piece of sailcloth which was in turn wrapped with tarred cordage. Manufacturer: Karl Bareuther

Rum cask
Rum (sugar cane spirit) was served on board to seamen as part of rations, but was also used for medical treatment.

40-gun frigate,
Great Britain, 1768

At the end of the 16th century, the term 'frigate' came to refer to relatively small and fast warships. They lacked high super-structures on the bow and the stern, im-proving their seaworthiness with respect to other ships of the time. Such frigates still were not a uniform ship type. The classic sailing frigate first appeared in the 1740s (model shown here). They were fully rigged and the deck was armed along its length with up to 44 cannons (rating system of the Royal Navy, 18th century). Large frigates could carry up to 300 men. While the larger warships were used in lines of battle, frig-ates were used instead for reconnaissance, as fast transport vessels and as commerce raiders.

The scenes on the model's deck show how the crew of the ship cleared the ship for battle. Scale: 1:50, Model maker: Hans-Joachim Holländer

7 ENGLAND AGAINST FRANCE

In the 18th century, England grew to be-come the dominant naval power. Starting in the late 17th century, France became its main rival. In addition to competition in world trade, during and after the French Revolution there were also ideological dif-ferences. All attempts by the French to end British supremacy at sea failed, however. In the famous Battle of Trafalgar

in October 1805, the British fleet won a significant victory over the allied French and Spanish forces. Napoleon's plans for an eventuela invasion of England were thus thwarted once an fo all.

Admiral Horatio Nelson (1758–1805) had an important role in England's victory. He repeatedly proved himself to be a brilliant tactician in battle. His victories brought him lasting fame not only in his British homeland but also abroad. Admiral Nelson was killed by a French bullet in the Battle of Trafalgar.

View of Deck 2
Historic sailing ships

**Life mask
of Horatio Nelson** (replica)

The HMS 'Foudroyant' was Nelson's flagship from 6 June 1799 to the end of June 1801. Two original cannons from on board the ship are on display in front of the entrance to our building.

HMS 'Victory' 1805 In the Battle of Trafalgar, the HMS 'Victory' was Nelson's flagship. Today the 'Victory' is a museum ship in Portsmouth. The sailing ship was never decommissioned and is thus the oldest ship in British service.
Scale 1:75, Model maker: Udo Flohr

Letter from Nelson to Sir William Hamilton, 4 March 1800. Starting in February 1800, Commodore Nelson participated in the blockade of the French forces at Malta on board the HMS 'Foudroyant'. In this letter, he asks his friend Sir William Hamilton (1730–1805), a diplomat at the court of King Ferdinand I of Naples, to request the deployment of four gunboats.

Letter from Napoleon Bonaparte (1769–1821) Here, Bonaparte issues orders to his adjutant Savary (1774–1833) to inspect defences and shipyards in Ostend and at Aragon and Vlissingen (Flushing). The letter is dated according to the second Republican Calendar as the 14th of Nivôse 12, equivalent to 3 January 1804.

Highlight: gundeck of a British corvette.
Bronze cannons, boarding swords, swivel guns. Here one can see what was needed for a battle in the days of Admiral Nelson.

Gundeck around 1800.
On the gundeck there is an original signal drum from the HMS Britannic, which fought at Trafalgar.

Portraits of Horatio Nelson and Emma Hamilton

Emma Hamilton (1765–1815) was the mistress of the (married) Admiral Nelson. Because of her beauty and her relations with prominent men, she was famous across Europe at the end of the 18th century.

English caricature

John Bull, the English equivalent of the German Michel, dines on one French fleet after another. An allusion to the many successes of the Royal Navy during the Napoleonic Wars.

One of the most dangerous routes in seafaring is the journey around Cape Horn. Here there are extreme weather conditions throughout the year. Storms with high wind speeds race from west to east through the straits between Tierra del Fuego and Graham Land in Antarctica. Any sailor who had conquered the Cape on a sailing ship enjoyed great respect. With the advent of steam navigation and the opening of the Panama Canal in 1914, fewer and fewer sailing ships travelled around Cape Horn. Aware of this turning point in history, a group of captains in St Malo (France) founded the exclusive Brotherhood of Cape Horners in 1937. After the Second World War this became an international organization. The association sought to promote and strengthen the ties of comradeship among captains who had proven themselves at the Cape as well as to commemorate their courage, their abilities and their ships. Its members were sailors who had rounded Cape Horn in the east-west direction (against the prevailing winds) in cargo sailing ships without propellers. Ordinary membership was open to captains and all those who had rounded the Horn as part of a crew and later earned a captain's licence. Extraordinary members were seamen who had rounded Cape Horn but had never been captains. The brotherhood existed internationally until 2003, but then dissolved due to aging of its members. Today the last living Cape Horners are over ninety years old. The decrease in cargo shipping by sail and the strict admission criteria of the AICH ('Amicale International des Capitaines Au Long Cours') meant that the club of Cape Horners had no prospect of continuing.

AICH membership card

of Wilhelm Lusthoff. The card identifies Wilhelm Lusthoff as a 'Malamok'. This means that he had rounded Cape Horn as a seaman but later acquired his captain's licence. Those who had rounded the stormy cape as captains could use the title 'Albatross'.

Four-masted barque 'L'Avenir', Belgium, 1908

The ship was commissioned by the Association Maritime Belge at the Rickmers shipyard and delivered as 'L'Avenir'. In 1932 the Finnish ship company Erikson purchased it and then gave it to Hapag in 1937. The ship was on a training voyage under its new name 'Admiral Karpfanger' when it went into distress south of Cape Horn in the spring of 1938. On 12 March at 6:05 A.M., the last radio contact was received. Scale: 1:50, Model maker: unknown

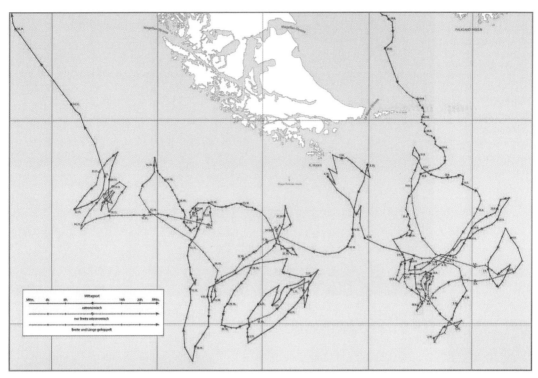

Flag of the Cape Horners
The symbol of the Cape Horners is the albatross. The brotherhood's flag shows an albatross's head with a rectangular metal ring in its beak. The image is based on a technique for capturing albatrosses, wherein a ring hook was baited and attached to a line. As long as the line was kept taut, the albatross ate the bait, and could no longer free itself from the ring. In this manner it was brought on board and then released. Killing an albatross, however, was considered taboo. It was said that the soul of a seaman who died at sea lived on in the form of an albatross.

Johannes Holst, (1880–1964)
'Pinnas von Laeisz untergehend' ('Pinnas of Laeisz sinking') Oil on canvas, 100x70 cm, 1946 Under dramatic clouds, the demasted 'Pinnas' fights with the sea. The full-rigged ship owned by the shipping company Laeisz was on a saltpetre mission between Germany and Chile.

On 26 April 1929 it was caught in a hurricane in the Cape Horn region and was demasted. The Chilean steamer 'Alfonso' was reached by radio and requested to help. All 25 crew members were saved before the ship sank.

The storm voyage of the 'Susanna'
The southern winter and spring of 1905 brought particularly heavy and persistent storms. If sailing ships from the Atlantic wanted to reach the west coast of South America, they needed a particularly long time to cross the Cape Horn region. The longest circumnavigation was that of Captain Christian Jürgens and his crew from the full-rigged 'Susanna' owned by the Hamburg shipping company G. J. H. Siemers & Co. They passed the 50th parallel in the Atlantic on the morning of 19 August and in the Pacific on the evening of 26 November. '50° to 50°' was the definition of a successful rounding of Cape Horn. The ship took 99 days for the journey. The chart shows the dramatic struggle of the crew to make it westward. During the 99 days of their stormy voyage they experienced wind forces 10 to 12 according to the Beaufort Wind Scale (violent storm to hurricane) during 40 percent of the watches, and forces 8 to 9 (gale force to storm) during another 25 percent of the watches. Despite the extreme conditions, Captain Jürgens reached his destination harbour of Caleta Buena (Chile) without losing a single man.

Stormy voyage of the 'Susanna'
99 days off Cape Horn

Thomas Buttersworth: 'A Moonlight Battle Scene between two armed Vessels'

'Störtebeker's skull'

9 PIRATES: VILLAINS OR HEROES?

Countless books and films have described pirates as mythical figures. We often connect the pirate's life with a romantic fantasy of freedom and adventure. The pirate is both a villain and a hero at the same time in these stories. The reality is different. Pirate attacks have always been a brutal affair. Pirates plundered, tortured and murdered. For most people, just the sight of the Jolly Roger pirate's flag could induce fear and terror. International maritime law and the spread of steam navigation brought piracy to a temporary end in the mid-19th century. Nowadays, however, piracy is again a threat. Certain coasts in east Africa and southeast Asia are considered particularly dangerous. Equipped with the latest technology, modern pirates capture yachts and even large container ships by force. They only release the ship and crew after receiving large ransom payments.

Historically, there was a difference between pirates and privateers. Until the 19th century, governments issued private ship-owners so-called letters of marque. These certificates authorized attacks on ships from enemy nations. The privateer was a kind of state-sponsored pirate who acted on behalf of his country.

Thomas Buttersworth (1768–1842): 'Moonlight Battle Scene between two armed Vessels' The painting is based on an old sailor's song. In a moonlit setting, a pirate ship attempts to escape to the open sea under full sail. Fire on the shore hints at a raid that took place. The ship is pursued and attacked by an English Coastguard cutter.

'Störtebeker's skull'
Skull of a pirate who was beheaded in Hamburg around 1400. The skull was found in 1878 in the Grasbrook district during construction of the Speicherstadt. Since the location of the find and its preparation indicate a famous personality, some suspect that it could be the skull of Klaus Störtebeker. Replica. The original is located at the Hamburg Museum.

Convoy ship 'Wapen von Hamburg', Germany, 1669. Since Hamburg merchant ships were continually seized by barbary corsairs, the Bürgerschaft (legislative assembly) decided to construct two convoy ships. The first was the 'Leopoldus Primus', and the second the 'Wapen von Hamburg'. Both successfully fought against the pirates under the command of the naval hero Berent Jakobsen Karpfanger (1622–1683). Scale: 1:75, Model maker: Martin Houska

Clipper 'Roger B. Taney' USA, 1833. The 'Roger B. Taney' was a Morris-Taney class clipper. With its sharp bow and a large sail area, the ships were exceptionally fast and were preferred for coastal protection. Due to its sailing characteristics, these clippers was also favoured by pirates and illegal slave traders. Scale: 1:54, Model maker: unknown

Galleon 'Golden Hind' England, 1577. The 'Golden Hind' (formerly the 'Pelican') served Sir Francis Drake (1540–1596) as an expedition and privateer ship during his legendary expedition into the Pacific. On the return voyage, Drake became the second captain to sail around the world, after Magellan. The model won a bronze medal from Naviga, the world organization for model ship building and model ship sport. Scale: 1:66, Model maker: Martin Houska

10 TALL SHIPS AND WINDJAMMERS

The term 'tall ship' refers to a multi-mast, mostly square-rigged sailing ship. The most well-known tall ships are the so-called windjammers ('to jam the wind'). Windjammers appeared in the second half of the 19th century, ending the era of the clipper. They were not only designed for speed, but also for the economical transport of bulk cargoes.

Windjammers already took advantage of the benefits of industrial production: hulls and masts made of iron or steel, steel cables for the rigging, and winches on deck to make work easier. The ships usually had three to four masts and were either rigged as barques or full-rigged. Designed for long journeys on the oceans, they were also

Barque 'Rickmer
Rickmers',
Germany, 1896

called 'Tiefwassersegler' in German (ships that sail in deep water). Windjammers were in direct competition with steamers, which had already begun to dominate many aspects of seafaring. Their domain were long distances that steamers still couldn't operate on without stopovers (they needed frequent stops in ports to stock up on coal). In the mid-20th century, the last cargo-carrying tall ships disappeared from the world's oceans. Today, windjammers serve as sail training or tourist ships.

Carolin Wehrmann (b. 1959), Clipper 'Coriolanus', England, Oil on canvas
The 'Coriolanus' was built in the Archibald McMillan & Son shipyard in Dumbarton in 1876 as a tea clipper for the Patton shipping company in London. Due to the opening of the Suez Canal and competition from steamers, she only made a single journey with tea cargo. Instead, the 'Coriolanus' became the queen of jute fibre shipping. Her speed was impressive from the outset, and in 1877 she made the journey between the Isles of Scilly and Calcutta in only 69 days – still a world record.

Tea clipper 'Cutty Sark' Roger Chapelet (1903–1995), Oil on canvas, 73.5 x 55 cm

Barque 'Rickmer Rickmers',
Germany, 1896
The 'Rickmer Rickmers' was built as a full-rigged ship in 1896 for Rickmers Reismühlen und Schiffbau AG at the Rickmers shipyard in Bremerhaven. In 1916, during the war, the neutral Portuguese

seized the ship and used it as a training ship under the name 'Sagres' starting in 1923. Since 1987 the 'Rickmer Rickmers' has been a museum ship in Hamburg.
Scale: 1:100, Model maker: unknown

Five-mast barque 'Potosi', Germany, 1895
After the 'Preussen', the 'Potosi' (both owned by F. Laeisz) was the fastest cargo sailing ship of all time. Built in 1895 at the Tecklenborg shipyard in Geestemünde, the ship was mainly used for saltpetre shipping. During WWI it was moored in Valparaiso and was purchased in 1923 by the Chilean ship-owner Gonzales Soffia. On 15 September 1925 fire broke out on board. The ship was completely destroyed.
Scale: 1:100, Model maker: unknown

Five-mast fully rigged ship 'Preussen',
Germany, 1902. The 'Preussen', owned by F. Laeisz, was the model of technical perfection among sailing ships. This sailing ship, built at the Joh. C. Tecklenborg shipyard in Geestemünde, was the longest pure sailing ship in history Her best 24-hour run was 426nm in 1904. After a collision with the 'Brighton' ferry in the English Channel, the ship had to be abandoned on 5 November 1910.
Scale: 1:100, Model maker: Jürgen Schill

Five-mast fully rigged ship 'Preussen'
Roger Chapelet
(1903–1995), Oil on canvas, 64.5 x 50 cm

Barque 'Rickmer Rickmers' Roger Chapelet (1903–1995), Oil on canvas, 65 x 51 cm

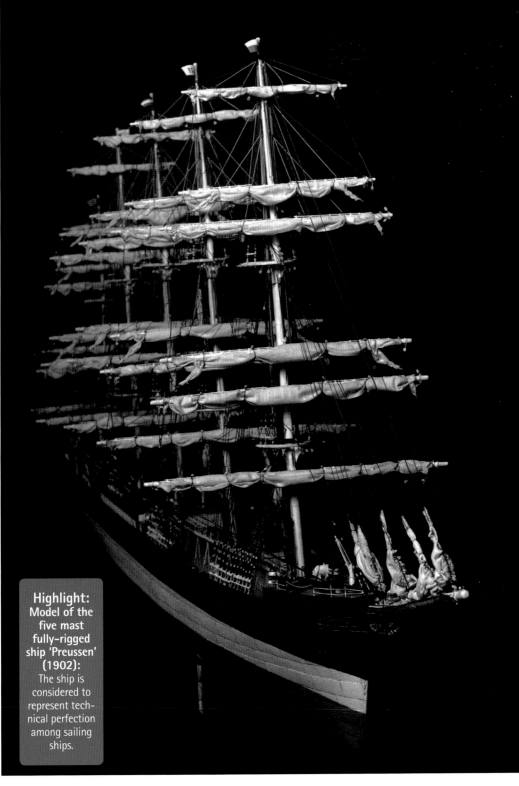

Highlight:
Model of the
five mast
fully-rigged
ship 'Preussen'
(1902):
The ship is
considered to
represent tech-
nical perfection
among sailing
ships.

SAIL TRAINING SHIPS

Sail training ships are tall ships used by merchant and military navies to train new personnel. They are either ships designed specifically for training or converted cargo sailing ships. Until after the Second World War, civilian sail training ships were also used for cargo voyages. The use of sailing ships to train officers resulted (in Germany) from a 1887 law that determined that an aspiring helmsman could only be admitted to exam if he had spent at least 12 month as an able bodied seaman aboard of sailing ships. However, since the number of sailing ships decreased due to the advent of steamships, shipping companies began operating sail training ships. Even today there are good reasons for the continued use of such ships: knowledge of weather conditions and the responsiveness of the ship, experience in commanding ships and analysis of the sea are basic elements of seafaring that can be learned quite intensively on sailing ships.

The Soviet training ship captain Oleg Wandenko said: 'We hold that nothing can replace the experiences of sailing. Confronted with the primal power of the sea, young seamen thus learn courage, persistence, skill and self-assertion. Sailing ships are schools for character!'.

'Schulschiff Deutschland', Germany, 1927. 'Schulschiff Deutschland' launched on 14 June 1927 from the Tecklenborg shipyard in Bremerhaven. It went on twelve voyages in the south Atlantic as well as in the North and Baltic seas. Due to the war she was deploied to Lübeck as a sail training ship in 1941. Later in the war she served as a hospital ship and continued to be since August 1945. After that she became a residential ship. Finally in 1952 she was again a sail training ship. Today 'Schulschiff Deutschland' is a museums ship in Bremen.
Scale 1:100; Model maker: Jürgen Schill

Highlight: painting of sail training ship 'Deutschland' (1927). Painter Adolf Bock creates the impression of a ghost ship approaching through the fog

Sail training ship 'Deutschland', Adolf Bock (1890–1968), oil on canvas, 88 x 66.5 cm

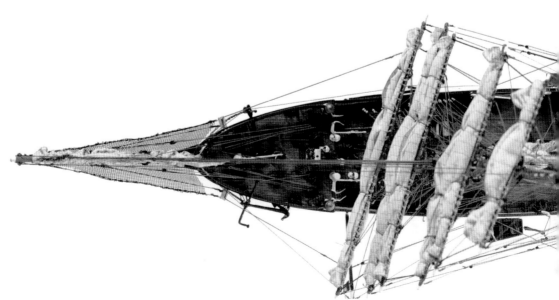

Three-mast barque 'Gorch Fock', Germany, 1958. On 23 August 1958, the 'Gorch Fock' launched at Blohm & Voss, Hamburg. It serves the German navy as a training ship. Its home port is Kiel. The ship is named to commemorate the German author Johann Kinau (pseudonym Gorch Fock), who wrote in his native Low German dialect. He was killed in 1916 during the Battle of Jutland (Battle of Skagerrak). It is the second ship to bear that name. The first 'Gorch Fock' was launched in 1933.
Scale: 1:75; Model maker: Erwin Brodtke

Training ship 'Danmark', Denmark 1932. The training ship 'Danmark' launched from the Nakskov Skibsvaerft shipyard on 19 November 1932 for the Ministry of Commerce, Trade and Shipping. In New York, the ship was surprised by the outbreak of war in 1939, and received orders not to sail back to Denmark. It only returned home after the end of the war and has since served as a training ship. Scale 1:100 Model maker: unknown

Training ship 'Amerigo Vespucci', Italy, 1931
This full-rigged ship launched on 22 February 1931 from the dockyard of Castellamare di Stabia. With its construction, the Italian navy found a way to combine tradition and modernity in ship design. On its exterior, the ship is reminiscent of 19th century ships of the Line. On the interior, however, modern standards were applied.
Scale: 1:84; Model maker: Bruno Kramp

'Schulschiff Deutschland',
Germany, 1927

HIGHLIGHTS ON DECK 3

The dugout marked in some cultures the beginning of complex wooden boat building after the last great Ice Age.

This filigree model of a Sambuk from Oman demonstrates a centuries-old tradition of ship craftsmanship.

'Hulls of Ships': This 1684 manuscript by William Keltridge represents the nascent increase in the application of scientific methods to the construction of ships.

'Architectura Navalis Mercatoria' ('Merchant Ship Construction') from 1768 is a standard work on ship design from the 18th century.

'La Salamandre' is an artfully crafted layer model of a mortar galiot.

An 1887 schematic of the steamer 'Virgilia' is one of the most beautiful plan drawings ever to come out of German shipyards.

Meyer-Werft, building the 'Superstar Leo' This large-format painting shows the newbuilding of a cruise ship.

Launching memorabilia of a Royal Navy battleship: the HMS 'Ocean', 5 July 1898.

Large-scale 1:20 model of one of the two four-cylinder, triple-expansion steam engines (port side) from the famous 'Titanic' of 1912.

Model of the first motor based on compressive self-ignition, developed by Rudolf Diesel in 1897.

Time-lapse documentation of the construction of the container ship 'Cosco Panama'. – How to build a ship in five minutes.

NAVAL CONSTRUCTION: FROM CRAFTSMANSHIP TO SCIENCE

The genesis of the intricate structure ship matured from craft to science in the course of millennia. Point source of the presentation in the museum is the shipbuilder's materials and tools, as well as different shipbuilding traditions such as the strake construction. From the latter arose the need to precisely plan a ship's hull. The practical application of scientific knowledge made this possible.

The breakthrough occured in the 17th century. Designers and client were now able to demonstrate in drawings and three-dimensional models exactly what requirements the ship had to fulfil and give the other an idea of the desired dimensions.

Since the middle of the nineteenth century design, construction and use of a ship, as well as the entire set-up of a ship yard, were tailored to the now predominant machine. The new propulsion system was accompanied by iron and steel, which were used in hull construction. Riveting hammers and welding equipment entered the work environment where the ship's carpenter trade had ruled before. In our day and time, the facilities of digital design and construction are crucial.

1 SHIPBUILDING MATERIALS

Wood: use of a valuable raw material

Hard woods such as oak, elm and teak or soft woods like pine, cedar and cypress were, depending on the construction tradition, the preferred types of wood for shipbuilding until they were replaced by iron and steel as the main shipbuilding material in the 19th c. An enormous amount of timber was used for shipbuilding. Up to 2,000 oak trees were felled to build a vessel of about 1,500 t. Imports of timber therefore very quickly became increasingly important for all shipyards. Even the Egyptians used cedar from the Levant. In the 17th and 18th c., entire forests were felled in Westphalia, Scandinavia and the Baltic states to provide timber for the major maritime powers. Only at a late stage was there any real appreciation of the knowledge or methods of wood processing that protected trees, which grew only slowly: in 1570, Queen Elizabeth I of England issued a prohibition on felling, thus ensuring the controlled planting of trees for shipbuilding. The saw mill for processing hard wood reduced the high wastage caused by splitting timber since the Late Middle Ages. Trees were bent during their growth phase so that they could be used later for e.g. compass timber. Timber was treated to protect it against decay. Various methods were used to protect the hulls of vessels against barnacles and worm infestation. Iron finally replaced parts of wooden ships with composite building from the mid-19th c. until vessels were built entirely of steel.

From boat to ship. High-tech craftsmanship

Early craft such as skin boats, reed boats and rafts had a simple structure but were nevertheless effective and invariably 'state-of-the-art'. With the growth of forests after the end of the Ice Age, the advent of massive, stable dugout canoes increased the variety of vessel types in, for instance, Central and Northern Europe. Later, a more complex wooden design facilitated the development from boat to ship. In the 3rd millennium BC, sickle-shaped ships made of Lebanon cedar plied the Nile. Vessels already used the power of the wind with square sails from the papyrus plant. Bulbous round ships with arched stem and stern posts equipped with lateen sails were built by shipyards in the Mediterranean. Fast rowing galleys were fitted with a ram. Their self-supporting hull shell was enlarged by putting planks on one another. The contact surfaces were joined with tenon and mortise and the planks secured with wooden dowels. The Vikings already built 'high-tech' products. With the aid of special measuring instruments, oak planks, hewn with an adze from a trunk along the grain of the wood, were combined like roof tiles to form a hull according to the clinker system. Thanks to its natural strength, cleft timber could be used to build a robust yet elastic structure.

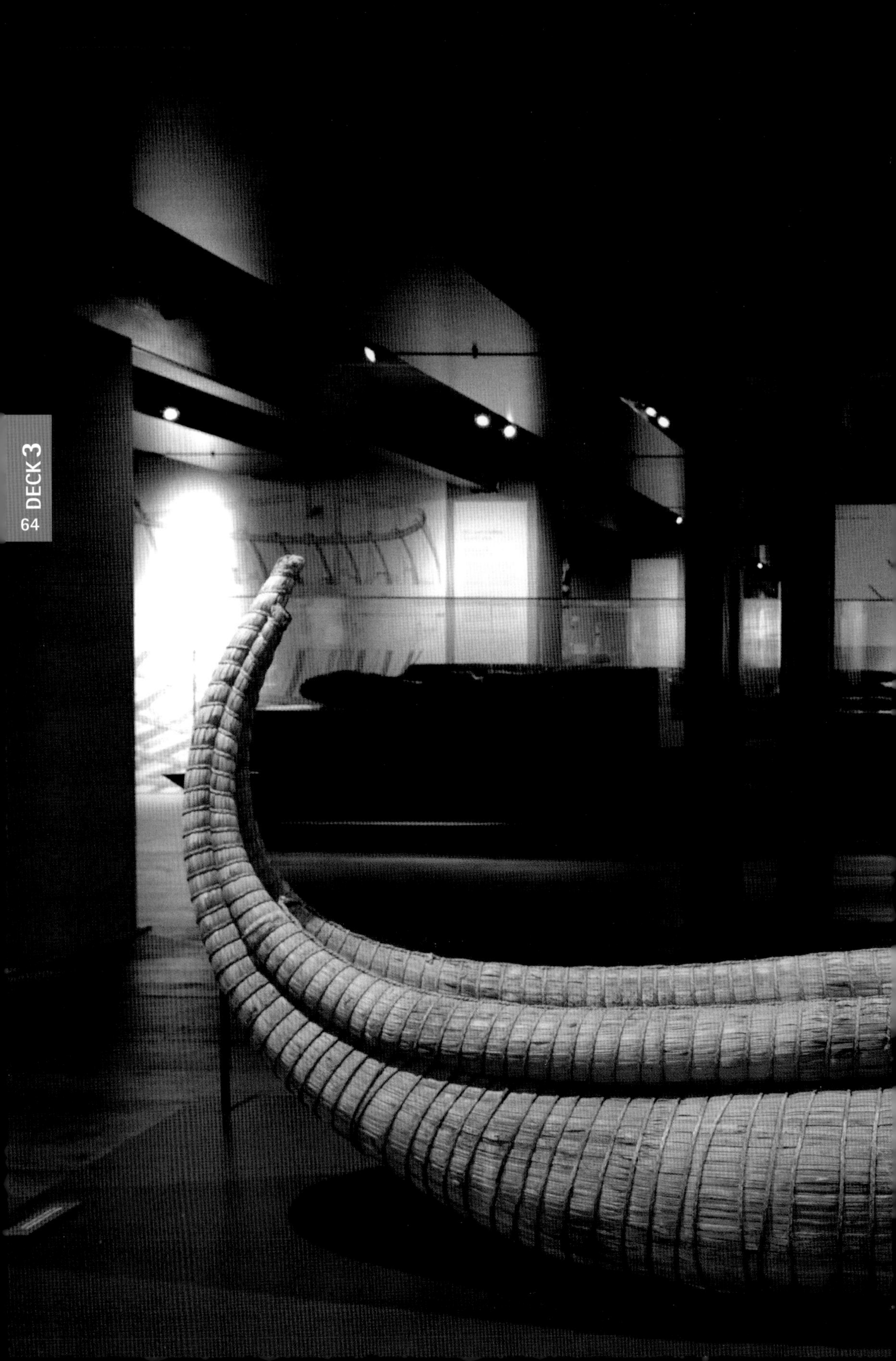

Boat made of reed bundles, Lake Titicaca, Bolivia/ Peru
These vessels consist of two cigar-shaped reed bundles ('S. tato-ra') that are bound tightly together with a core bundle. This design has two smaller reed bundles on the upper sections that basically form a bulwark. Paddles and sails made of reed mats are used as propulsion for these fishing or transport boats.

2 EARLY VESSELS

Dugout

Dugouts are among the oldest wooden watercraft. In northern Europe there is prove of dugouts since the beginning of forest growth after the end of the Ice Age. Oak or linden trunks, with as few branches as possible, were felled near the waterside and then hollowed out with fire, by gouging and by wedging. The shortened trunks were usually provided with a semi-circular bulkhead so that the wood did not split. The hollowed-out trunk could be widened by means of spreading with cross bars in order to improve stability and to increase the transport capacity. The dugout shown here, found in Geesthacht on the river Elbe, is a 'boat' formed in this manner using spreading crossbars. According to radiocarbon dating, it comes from the Early Middle Ages around 650 A.D. and thus is a more recent representative of its kind (on loan from the Archäologisches Museum Hamburg).

The Nydam Boat, around 320 AD.

The original was found and excavated in 1863 from the Nydam bog in Denmark. The hull of this war vessel, built in 320 AD and presumably sunk later as a sacrificial offering, had clinker construction. The planks were joined together like roof tiles with iron rivets. Wool and a tarlike substance served as a sealant. The oak ribs were fixed to the planks with ropes. Propulsion was accomplished by up to 36 rowers, using straps that operated in oar-racks. The nearly 25-metre-long and 3.20-metre-wide vessel had neither a mast nor a sail. The original is located today at the Archäologisches Landesmuseum Schloß Gottorf near Sleswig. Scale: 1:20, model maker: Hans Brechelt

Cross section of the Gokstad ship,

around 900. The longitudinal and transverse cross section up to the mast's mount shown here gives a three-dimensional impression of a Viking ship at a 1:18 scale. The clinker-built structure of oak planks was assembled with iron nails and sealed with pitch-soaked animal hair. In the foreground, ship construction tools and various ship equipment.
Scale: 1:18, model maker: Ingo Drössler

Hjortspring Boat, around 350 BC

Model of the approximately 18-metre-long boat found in the Hjortspring bog on the Danish island of Alsen. The hull planks, made of linden wood, were overlapped in clinker style. They are sewn with bast (inner bark fibre) and sealed with a resinous putty. The antler-like stems probably served to protect the hull. The 530-kilogram boat was powered by about 20 paddles. The Hjortspring Boat matches many images found on petroglyphs.
Scale ~1:16

Dhoni from the Maldives

A dhoni is a traditional fishing and transport boat from the Maldives. Dhoni hulls are made from coconut wood, while the sails are made from coconut fibres. The shape of a dhoni is reminiscent of Arabic dhows.

War canoe from Tahiti

In April 1774 the British seafarer and explorer James Cook (1728–1779) observed a number of these colourfully decorated double-hulled canoes in Tahiti. At around 36 metres, they were almost as long as his own ship, the 'Resolution'. The crew of the canoes used single-sided paddles. The raised platform served as a command post for the chief and his retinue.
Scale 1:75, model maker: Lothar Finger

Waka Taua, Maori culture, New Zealand

'Waka Taua' means 'war canoe' in the Maori language. Like a dugout, the hull was either carved out of a tree trunk or was assembled from up to three hollowed out sections connected by tongue and groove joints and lashes. The boats' hulls were richly decorated with ornaments. Scale 1:75, model maker: Lothar Finger

Jangada from Brazil

Jangadas are wooden rafts made from strong tree trunks (from piuva trees). They continue to be used as fishing vessels on the Atlantic coast of Brazil. The hull of this fast sailing vessel is bound together with wooden crossbars and lashings. The sail is fixed to a light mast with a boom. Scale ~1:10

Sambuk ('shu'i') from Oman

Typical features of this variant of a dhow are the low, almost scimitar-like bow and the towering rear section. The carvel-planked hull is sewn together. The teak planks are nailed together with the help of stencils and caulked with palm fibres soaked in fish oil. The ribs are made from acacia. Sambuk construction was based solely on experience that was passed down from generation to generation. Scale ~1:65

Construction of a junk

Diorama (scale 1:200) of a yard with a seagoing junk on the stocks in northern China. The barrel-shaped hull has a flat, protruding bow. The construction material was typically fir or pine wood with lashed carvel planking. Chinese shipbuilders knew about the benefits of transverse bulkheads for the safety and stability of a ship's hull.

Model of a Carrack, 15th–16th century

The term 'carrack' in the 15th century indicated a large ship. In the Iberian region, vessels of this type were so common that they took on the name 'nau' (a Portuguese word for 'ship'). The carrack was a fusion of Mediterranean and northern European ship construction. The common ancestor was probably the cog. The skeleton-built hull and lateen sail on the rear mast originated in the Mediterranean. The square sail and stern rudder were inherited from northern European shipbuilding tradition.

The combination of both traditions brought about the full-rigged ship. Contemporary rulers quickly recognized the value of such 'tall' ships. Heavy armament with guns inside the hull behind gunports was now technically feasible. The high forecastle equipped with a grappling hook made it possible to hold enemy ships fast and board them. Discoveries, conquest, war and maritime trade became possible with the carrack. It was

Highlight: filigree model of a sambuk from Oman demonstrates centuries-old ship craftsmanship.

DECK 3

67

the first maritime 'global player'. The model is based on a contemporary woodcut from 1468 by the Flemish goldsmith Willem A Cruce.

Scale ~1:50, model maker: Martin Koschwitz

3 WILLIAM KELTRIDGE, 'HULLS OF SHIPS'

William Keltridge, Hulls of Ships, 1684
In 1684, William Keltridge, a ship carpenter from Portsmouth, worked on a manuscript book called 'Hulls of Ships' that contained standardized dimensions for the ships of the Royal Navy and illustrated plans for 4th, 5th and 6th 'rate' (class) frigates and sloops based on these dimensions. Following the precedent set by Sir Anthony Deane, Keltridge was one of the first to draw the underwater lines of a ship. Although his scientific work consisted primarily of the application of geometric forms, his book already contains sheer plans as well as fore and aft views with hull lines and frames. The drawings were accompanied by tables with ship data. Subsequently, designing a ship before building it became a matter of course in the wake of Keltridge's work, and this led to the application of scientific approaches to shipbuilding and to the use of calculations, drawings and models for the determination of hull shape, speed and stability. Keltridge's work is part of a revolutionary change in which craftsmanship was combined with scientific planning.

Keltridge Drawings, 1684
In his manuscript and especially in his drawings, William Keltridge made an approach towards scientific methods for ship design. A trademark of Keltridge's work is the non-tangentially joined stem post to the keel. The coloured drawings are obviously related to the reorganization of the Royal Navy under the Chief Secretary to the Admiralty Samuel Pepys who supervised and supported the famous first shipbuilding program, the 'Establishment of Men and Guns', of 1677.

4 SHIPBUILDING TOOLS

Hand carpentry and computer-controlled manufacturing. As long as wood remained the main shipbuilding material, the typical tools of the carpenter were used at shipyards. They hardly differed in principle from the equipment used for e.g. house building, although the shipbuilder had to work much more precisely because of the symmetry of the curved hull form. Also special tools were required to make the hull watertight.

The main tools for building wooden ships were hatchets, axes, saws and drills. The shape of these developed in line with technical progress, depended on the hardness of the wood or were a result of a change from one shipbuilding tradition to another. The ancient T-shaped axe thus quickly lost significance when splitting was ousted by sawing; a sawn plank requires less finishing than cleft timber. The saw mill, an invention of the late Middle Ages, facilitated the transition from clinker to carvel building in Northern Europe. Hard woods such as oak could now be used just

Highlight: 'Hulls of Ships'
This 1684 manuscript by William Keltridge represents the nascent increase in the application of scientific methods in the construction of ships.

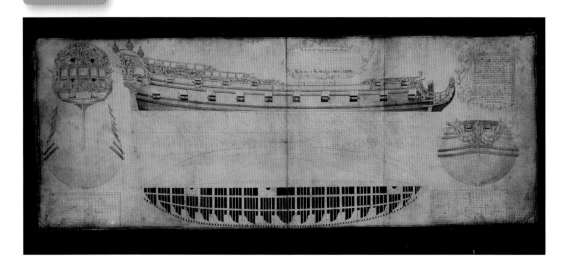

as effectively as Mediterranean soft woods for hull construction on frames.

The tools used to produce hulls of iron and steel are totally different from those required for wooden ships. Riveting hammers and later welding equipment, plasma torches and computer-controlled laser welding units conquered the shipyards.

Welding technique: gas metal arc welding

The term welding means 'permanent joining of components under application of heat or pressure, with or without filler materials'. The most commonly used method is fusion welding. The parts to be joined are heated until they are liquefied so that they mix together. When cool,

Gas metal arc welding

Laser beam welding

they are firmly connected to each other. The gas metal arc welding method is presented here. An electrical arc between the filler and the components serves as a heat source. The welding point is protected

from oxidation by a shielding or mixed gas. Oxidation would reduce the quality of the weld. (Images from the training workshop of Blohm + Voss, Hamburg)

Welding technique: Laser beam welding

Laser beam welding functions without using a filler. Pieces of metal are joined by casting them punctually and momentarily by laser beam. Welding by laser beam has the advantage of higher welding rates in comparison to manual welding; it can be operated by computer on a welding line. (Images of laser beam welding at Blohm + Voss shipyard, Hamburg.)

5 SHIPBUILDING BECOMES A SCIENCE

Design on paper

There are few early written sources for shipbuilding. Only the increase in literacy in the Late Middle Ages led, for instance, to technical subjects being fixed in contractual form between customer and contractor. The first writings with ship designs were also compiled. This development started in the Mediterranean region, where from the 7th c. shipbuilders built 'on frames', for which the ribbing, or the exact hull form, had to be predetermined, in contrast to the traditional shell construction. Planning was necessary. The first important treatise on this was compiled by the Venetian Giorgio Timbotta da Modo (ca. 1450). Later, during the Enlightenment, the collected knowledge of the science of shipbuilding was conveyed by, for instance, Anthony Deane (1670), William Keltridge (1684), Leonard Euler (1749) and particularly Fredrik Henrik af Chapman (1768). A few decades later, it was a matter of course for the Englishman David Steel to design a hull on paper.

'Architectura Navalis Mercatoria'

('Merchant Ship Construction'), 1768
Fredrik Henrik af Chapman was born in Gothenburg, and was the son of a master shipbuilder from Yorkshire. He learned his father's profession and combined crafts-manship with scientific rigour. In 1768, his opus magnum 'Architectura Navalis Mercatoria' was published, for which his nephew Lars Bogman prepared the copperplate engravings. In 1775, Chapman published the 'Tractat om Skepps-Byggeriet' ('Treatise on Shipbuilding'), which added to the content of 'Architectura Navalis Mercatoria'.

'Alfred', 1778

The hull of the 3rd rate English ship 'Alfred' is planked with copper plates up to its waterline. Copper plating was an expensive but effective method to protect wooden ship to protect the underwater hull of a wooden ship from fouling and worm infestation. Mixtures of resin, tar and turpentine were less effective. However, their white hue was a common feature of the hulls of ships during the 18th century.
Scale 1:48, model maker M. Saville Smithin

Schiff auf der Helling ('Ship on the Slipway'), after 1750

The model shows the fully planked hull of a 3rd rate ship of the Royal Navy after 1750. Noteworthy features are the launching cradle as well as the auxiliary masts used for the abundant flag decoration typical for launching ceremonies. This 1:96 scale model is based on contemporary dioramas.

Teaching model for shipbuilders,

around 1890
This mock-up model, about 120 years old, was used as a demonstration object for shipbuilders in training. It shows the deli-cate-appearing wooden anatomy of an English second rate around 1700.
Scale ~1:72

Brigantine 'Leon', 1880

The brigantine 'Leon', here on a representa-tional slipway, was built in 1880 at Larvik, Norway. According to the entry in Lloyd's Register, she displaced 302 tonnes, was 110,7 ft (33.7 m) long and 28 ft (8.5 m) wide. She is a typical representative of the cargo ships of the North and Baltic Sea area in the 19th century. Scale 1:96, model maker: P.J. Puttock

'Cressy', Blackwall frigate, 1843

The term 'Blackwall frigate' refers on the one hand to the main London shipyard of the English East India Company. It also refers to large, fast passenger and cargo carrying merchant ships lacking high super-structures and a stern gallery. Those vessels were as swift as the Navy's frigates. This model made of polished mahogany is at 1:48 scale. Model maker: Braithwaite

Launch diorama, 18th century.

During the second half of the 18th century, ship models were often part of a diorama

showing a launching ceremony. This richly detailed model of an English frigate is mounted on an extendable box frame. The launching cradle with trigger mechanism was used only for display purposes. In those times, larger ships were built in a dry dock and were 'launched' by floating the dock. Scale 1:96, model maker: Neil Stephens

Yacht, 17th century

'Jachten' were originally pleasure crafts for affluent Dutch citizens in the 17th century. The original regatta sailing yachts had a rather belly-shaped hull. The model shown here, a yacht with Dutch-style leeboards, bears the insignia of the Russian Empire.

6 MODEL SHIPBUILDING

Ship models: Vital design tools

Ship models originally served religious purposes, for instance as votive offerings or grave furnishings. Since the middle of the 17th century they have been an important aid for designers. This went hand in hand with the introduction of scale drawings. Less detailed block models made from one piece or roughly worked half models of wood were used for deciding on a newbuilding or conversion. While the significance of block models declined over time, half models have remained in use in shipbuilding up to the present day. They can be made quickly and are ideal for planning the plates of the shell of steel ships. Shipbuilding research institutes use the mostly yellow test tank model hulls for simulating the propulsion performance of vessels. And filigree pipe models offer a three-dimensional impression of engine rooms.

Ship models have also been made artistically as decorative objects since the 17th century, the most famous examples being the Navy Board models of the British Admiralty. These gems with their framing and finely detailed superstructure took a long time to build, and indeed the outlay involved could be compared with that required for the original. The shipyard models usual today came into fashion in the mid-19th century. They demonstrate the capabilities of a shipbuilding company, while shipping lines use them for advertising purposes and museums for illustrating the history of shipping.

'La Salamandre', 1752

This 1:48 scale model is not only of interest because it represents an unusual vessel, a bomb ketch. It is also an outstanding feat of craftsmanship to present the hull horizontally divided, and to show many details and internal fittings. 'La Salamandre' was built between 1752–1754 at Toulon, from plans by Joseph Marie Blaise Coulomb. The model is based on a reconstruction by Jean Boudriot and Hubert Berti.

'Henny Pickenpack'

'Jürgensby'

Johanna'

Tugboat 'Emil'

Half model of a steam-powered fishing boat

'Henny Pickenpack', 1914
Scale 1:50; shipyard: Wichhorst-Werft, Hamburg, yard number 255

Half model of the passenger ship 'Jürgensby', 1966

Scale: 1:25; shipyard Husumer Schiffswerft, yard number 1245

Half model of the three-mast barque 'Johanna', 1880

Scale 1:25; shipyard: H.C. Stülcken & Sohn, Hamburg, yard number 23

Half model of the tugboat 'Emil', 1913

Scale 1:50; shipyard: Joh. Oelkers Schiffswerft, Hamburg, yard number 404

'Java', 1811

This launch diorama apparently shows the 'Java', built in 1811 at Calcutta and entered into Lloyd's Register in 1813 for Paxton & Co. In the foreground, in front of the slipway, material such as shipbuilding wood, masts, spreaders, blocks, cordage rolls and casks can be seen.

Highlight:
'La Salamandre' is an artfully crafted layer model of a bomb ketch.

Profile and draught, 'Virgilia', 1887
Flensburger Schiffbau-Gesellschaft, yard number 91
This ship owned by the shipping company Adolph Kirsten has been missing since 6 August 1890. It was last seen after leaving the Strait of Magellan on a voyage from Hamburg to Valparaiso, Chile.

Stern section of a cargo ship
Stern section of a motorized cargo ship with ice horn and Simplex balanced rudder; weight 40.6 tonnes. Scale 1:15

Stern section of ferry
Stern section of a ferry with a spade rudder; weight 34 tonnes. Scale 1:15

Stern section of a trailing suction hopper dredger
Stern section of a hopper suction dredger with Kort-nozzle, weight 108.5 tonnes. Scale 1:15

Stern section of an ocean-going tugboat
Stern section with ducted propeller for towing, ocean-going tugboat; weight 82.1 tonnes. Scale 1:15

Pipe model
Modern shipbuilding, which is now accomplished on computers with CAD graphics, relied until just a few years ago on model making. Here the engineering facilities of a ship of the Federal German navy are shown at 1:10 scale. This is a model of a class 745 ('Stollergrund') multipurpose military research vessel, built in 1988–1990, at Kröger shipyard, Rendsburg. Frames 11–35 are shown.

7 SHIP CONSTRUCTION LOGISTICS
The shipyard. From workshop to 'interface management'.
According to the 'Allgemeines Wörterbuch der Marine' by Johann Hinrich Röding (1796), a shipyard is a 'place located near the water set up for shipbuilding, where there are usually several slipways or stocks,

where vessels can be built and hoisted and launched.' This description still applies today, although the structure of yard operators has completely changed. The transition from craft to industrial production and the increasing technical complexity of the ship required a completely new organisation for shipyard operation. For a long time, shipyards remained places at which vessels were built from keel to truck as 'total work of art'. In the Second World War, however, the need for fast series production prompted the development of an efficient construction method. At American shipyards, for instance, the famous 'Liberty' ships were produced in several, identically large 'work packages'. This was a trailblazing innovation. Today, shipyards or shipyard associations build hulls in subassemblies and modules, as well as acting as 'interface managers' for a large number of suppliers and fitters. Skilled workers, engineers and designers have replaced the craftsmen of yesteryear.

Goss, Sawyer & Packard shipyard, Bath (Maine), around 1870
1:48 scale diorama of a three-masted barque or full-rigged ship in frames. Founded in 1866, this shipyard was one of the largest yards for wooden shipbuilding in the US. Captain Guy C. Goss invested in innovation with steam-powered wood processing. His Goss Marine Iron Works for steam engines was underfinanced, however. Together with the shipyard, it was acquired in 1888 by Bath Iron Works.

Shipbuilding at the Joh. C. Tecklenborg shipyard around 1912
The photograph shows the framing of the stern of the 'Johann Heinrich Burchard' at the shipyard of Joh. C. Tecklenborg in Geestemünde (Bremerhaven). This passenger vessel of the Hamburg American Line, launched on February 10th 1914, was the largest ship yet to have been built by Tecklenborg shipyard (as yard No. 256). Until 1938, the ship bore the name 'Reliance'.

Bridge structure MS 'Ariana', 1988
In 1988, the J.J. Sietas KG shipyard in Hamburg-Neuenfelde delivered an unusual new building to the Schiffahrtskontor Altes Land (SAL) company. MS 'Ariana' was intended to carry parts of the 'Ariane IV' satellite-launching rocket from Europe to Kourou in French Guiana. This detailed model shows the bridge structure of the ship. 1:100 scale, model maker: Jürgen Hinrichsen

Meyer-Werft, building the 'Superstar Leo' H.D. Tylle (b. 1954), Oil on canvas, 192 x 160 cm

Double-hulled tanker 'Manitou', 1985
The '1986 Ship of the Year' was designed with a double hull. In addition to greater security in the event of an accident, the cargo was also kept at a constant temperature. The Lindenau shipyard in Kiel, where the ship was constructed, was a leader in the development of double-hulled tankers until its bankruptcy in 2008.
1:100 scale, model maker: Günter Schmidt

'Railship III' rail ferry, 1990
The Schichau Seebeckwerft AG shipyard in Bremerhaven already had over 100 years' experience in rail ferry construction when 'Railship III' was delivered in 1990. This is a notable example of specialization in shipbuilding. The ferry has three decks and was the largest vessel of its kind when it was launched.
1:00 scale, model maker: Günter Schmidt

Launching memorabilia
HMS 'Ocean', 5 July 1898
This wooden box contains memorabilia from the launch ceremony of the British battleship 'HMS Ocean'. This battleship of the Royal Navy's 'Canopus' class was

Highlight:
Meyer-Werft (shipyard), reconstruction of the 'Superstar Leo' – the large-format painting shows the building of a cruise ship.

launched on July 5th 1898 at Devonport Dockyard. During World War One the ship sank after striking a mine off the Gallipoli peninsula on 18 March 1915.

Launch memorabilia
MS 'Peter Rickmers', July 9th 1993
Commemoration of the launching of the Motorship 'Peter Rickmers' at Stocznia SA shipyard for the shipping company Bertram Rickmers GmbH & Cie., Hamburg. The yard No. B 183-II/10 of the Szczecin shipyard later sailed as 'ZIM Mexico III' for ZIM Integrated Shipping, Israel, under the flag of Antigua and Barbuda; the ship manager was Rickmers shipping company.

8 THE HAMBURG SHIP MODEL BASIN (HAMBURGISCHE SCHIFF-BAUVERSUCHSANSTALT, HSVA)
HSVA is regarded as one of the leading establishments of its type worldwide. As an engineering office with technically sophisticated testing facilities, it is a service provider for shipyards and shipping lines. Hydrodynamic tests are carried out with the famous yellow models in its large model basin tank, 300 metres long. The hulls built true to scale seven to twelve metres long are produced in HSVA's own carpenter's shop with computer-supported design and fitted with propeller(s) and measuring instruments. In series of tests, e.g. the required propulsion

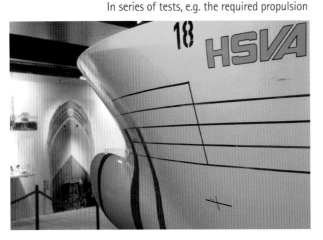

performance of a ship is determined. For this purpose, a towing carriage connected with a ship model simulates different speeds. The towing tank is also equipped with a wave generator to enable it to carry out further tests on ship safety in a seaway. The manoeuvring testing device makes it possible to move vessels or other objects on the water surface or submerged and measure the hydrodynamic forces and moments. Finally, the ice tank at HSVA enables researchers to study the resistance, required performance and manoeuvring behaviour of icebreaking ships relative to varying ice thicknesses, as well as measure e.g. forces on offshore structures in various ice conditions.

9 MECHANICAL ENGINEERING
The ship propeller.
Propulsion with screw propellers
The screw was used as a means of propulsion for watercraft even before the introduction of the engine. However, only the combination of mechanical energy and propeller brought an effective solution. The development of the most suitable screw form for a specific vessel remained subject to protracted and initially purely empirical tests. Sometimes, however, chance also lent a helping hand: when in 1836 Francis Pettit Smith (1808-74), an inventive sheep farmer, tested an Archimedean screw with a shaft and two complete turns of a single blade, a piece of the blade broke off – and his boat then went faster!
Along with Smith, a leading pioneer of the modern ship propeller was Josef Ressel (1793-1857) from Austria. The 'Königlich-Kaiserlicher Marine-Forstintendant' tested a double-threaded Archimedean screw with a half turn in 1829. Serious problems encountered with the steam engine of his ship 'Civetta' and competition from a paddle steamer line, however, prompted the secret police to prohibit further trials. In 1836, the Swedish engineer and inventor John Ericsson (1803-89) obtained a patent for a contra-rotating double screw with helical segments, which he successfully marketed in the USA. The theory of screw propulsion was developed after its practical application: only in 1865 did the scientists Macquorn Rankine and William Froude understand the physics of the ship propeller.

The steam engine
Until the mid-19th century, the force of the wind dominated ship propulsion. Then powerful steamers steadily replaced tra-

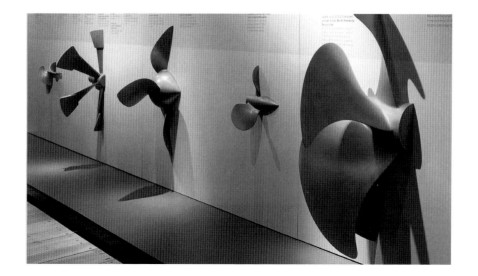

ditional sailing. Planning, construction and use of a ship changed according to the requirements of the new propulsion engines. The single-cylinder steam engine was developed into the more efficient compound engines in the 1880s. It enabled expansion of the steam in several stages and produced more steam power with less coal consumption. The model of the triple expansion engines on the 'Titanic' of 1912 highlights this breakthrough in the development of coal-powered steam engines. The next technical breakthrough in marine propulsion came soon afterwards. Powerful steam-driven rotating turbines took the place of piston engines on fast steamers and warships towards the end of the 19th century. The famous 'Titanic' also had a steam turbine of this type as an additional propulsion engine.

Engine of the fast steamer 'Deutschland', 1900. This model built by Karl-Friedrich Pohlmann shows one of the two quadruple expansion engines (portside) on the fast steamer 'Deutschland'. The engine's output was about 17,000 HP. In July 1900, the 'Deutschland' won the 'Blue Ribbon' for the fastest east-to-west crossing of the Atlantic, with a speed of 22.42 knots.

Highlight: large 1:20 scale model of one of the two four-cylinder triple expansion steam engines (portside) of the famous 'Titanic' of 1912.

Engine (portside) RMS 'Titanic', 1912. This model shows one of the two four-cylinder triple expansion steam engines on the 'Titanic', which sank in 1912. Taking nearly 15 bar steam pressure, each of the two engines indicated 15.000 HP. In addition, the ship had a steam turbine as its third engine. The richly detailed model was made by Karl-Friedrich Pohlmann. Scale 1:20

Components of a Bristol Proteus type gas turbine, 1962
Gas turbines are special internal combustion engines. Air is sucked in, compressed, mixed with fuel and burned; then in a turbine, the combustion gases expand and thermal energy is converted into kinetic energy. Gas turbines are used to propel airplanes and, due to their high power density, smaller, fast-moving ships and boats.
The Bristol Proteus-type unit shown here was installed on a fast patrol boat of the Bundesmarine that was delivered in 1962 from the British shipyard Vosper & Co. It reached speeds of up to 50 knots. Proteus-type gas turbines delivered about 4,260 HP. Its weight is about 1.3 tons. The turbine is a gift of the Rolls Royce company.

However the ship vibrated so strongly at high speeds that it took on the nickname 'Cocktail Shaker'. Scale 1:20

Engine of a paddle steamer, 19th century
A two-cylinder, horizontal engine is supplied with steam by a locomotive boiler. The engine drives two side paddlewheels, whose paddle blades ('floats') are attached to the rim of the wheel and pivot in response to a moving lever. Thus, they are always in an optimal thrust position.

Highlight: model of Rudolf Diesel's 1897 first compression-based self-ignition engine.

First diesel engine, 1897
This model was produced in the training workshop of Maschinenfabrik-Augsburg-Nürnberg (MAN). In cooperation with the engineer Rudolf Diesel (1858–1913) and the company Fr. Krupp, MAN introduced this heat engine based on compression-induced self-ignition. Thus began a new era of ship propulsion technology.
Scale 1:5

Wärtsilä–Sulzer 8RT–flex 96c diesel engine, 2004
The Sulzer RT-flex 'common-rail' eight-cylinder engine by Wärtsilä is used in modern diesel ship propulsion systems. The unit, with an output of 45,760 kW, has electronically controlled fuel injection. This has several advantages over ordinary diesel engines. It guarantees smoke-free operation at any speed; the 'common-rail' injection allows the engine to be run slowly, at only ten percent of the nominal engine speed of 102 rpm. Fuel consumption is relatively low, and ordinarily requires maintenance every three years. An eight-cylinder version of the engine has been used in small container ships since October 2004. The first ship was the 'Lars Mærsk' (3,700 TEU) of the Danish shipping company A.P. Møller-Mærsk, built

Deutsche Werft
Albert Wenk
(1863–1934),
tempera,
50x64cm

by the Odense Steel Shipyard A/S in Lindø.
1:16 scale

10 SHIPBUILDING IS AN ART

Polar planimeter, around 1930
Planimeters are analogue computers which can be used to measure areas. One arm of the planimeter is fixed and then the other arm is used to trace (in the clockwise direction) the border of the area to be evaluated. The area is calculated by integration, read off from the dial, and multiplied by a factor provided in a table to give the final result. Until just a few years ago, planimeters were indispensable tools for the measurement of areas for ship design. The device was manufactured by the company R. Reiss GmbH, Liebenwerda.

French curves ('Hamburg set')
Shipyard technical drawing studios had many different sets of French curves for their various needs. The 'German set' consists of 35 curves, the Hamburg set has 44 curves, and the Bremen set has 5 curves. They are made of either boxwood or pear wood, or cast from synthetic resin.

Building the 'Cosco Panama', time-lapse documentation
In December 2004, the keel of the 2,700 TEU container ship 'Cosco Panama' was laid down by Blohm + Voss in Hamburg. The filmmaker Timo Kurrat and Max C. Moos documented the construction with two time-lapse cameras. Over the course of 12 months, a picture was taken every minute, from the first weld seam until the maiden voyage on the North Sea.

Highlight: time-lapse documentation of construction of the container ship 'Cosco Panama' – ship construction in five minutes.

11 SAILING: FROM A ROYAL PASTIME TO A RECREATIONAL SPORT FOR THE MASSES

The yachting section is located in the wing near the lift. You may reach this area through a glass door. This way also leads to the library. Numerous items pertaining to the history of yachting can be found in the exhibition hall.

Pleasure yachts and racing yachts

The 'yacht' vessel type originating in the Netherlands was at the end of the 16th c. mostly a small fast ship carrying persons of high rank. The 'speel-jachten' with leeboard and often flat hull bottom became popular among the well-to-do around the mid-17th c. The Dutch delight in competitive sailing also inspired the British royal family to indulge in this pastime. The 'Royal Thames Yacht Club', founded in 1775, organised regattas for boats with a hull shape based on that of the cutter, deployed by the navy to hunt smugglers. Cutters had a relatively lean hull with a large draught, a mast and a bowsprit. The American 'sloop' was based on another design concept, oriented to east

coast fishing boats with a long hull with a low draught. The elegant boats were given a centreboard to enable them to sail better close to the wind with a large sail area. When competitive sailing for pleasure became a sport towards the end of the 19th c., internationally valid measurement systems and ratings led to the development of the modern regatta yacht.

The 'Golden Age' of competitive yachting

The 'golden age' of yachting lasted from the beginning of the 19th c. to the outbreak of the First World War. Regattas have been regularly held on the Solent off Cowes, the summer residence of the British royal family, since 1826. Cowes Week established itself as a fashionable social event in mid-August. In 1851, the 'America' challenged British yachts for the first time to an international race. The history of modern regattas began with the America's Cup off Cowes. Kaiser Wilhelm II was a constant guest in Cowes from 1889. The German monarch successfully participated with his 'Meteor' in the regatta scene as rival of the British royal family. The Kaiser's passion for every aspect

of maritime life contributed greatly to the popularising of sailing in Germany, particularly in the context of the event designated 'Kieler Woche' from 1894. Sailing began in the USA in the 19th c. as a pastime of the captains of industry. It became a mass sport with the first Olympic sailing competitions in 1900.

'Meteor' racing 'Britannia'
accompanied by 'Kaiseradler' and 'Victoria and Albert' David Brackman Oil on canvas, 75x116cm

HIGHLIGHTS ON DECK 4

Fez for crew members of Muslim faith
in the Austro-Hungarian navy.

Portrait of Hermann Gutschow,
the first surgeon general of the German Navy.

Viking sword
– a very rare, early example with pattern-welded blade.

The painting 'Gewehrreinigen im Batteriedeck eines Großkampfschiffes'
('Cleaning of Weapons on the Gun Deck of a Capital Ship') is one of the few images to document the life of the crew.

Baton of Großadmiral Henning von Holtzendorff
– one of only four Grand Admiral batons from the German Empire. Two of them are located at the IMMH.

Russian Saint Stanislaus medal
– a rare and valuable distinction for a German admiral, awarded in 1902.

Standard of the German emperor around 1900.
The flag was only hoisted when the Emperor was aboard.

UNIFORMS, ARMS, DECORATIONS AND LIFE ON BOARD

The 4th floor is dedicated to the routine and to the hierarchy on board ships and shows naval uniforms, insignia and small arms. Rank and specialization can be read from a uniform – they are important symbols and elements of the organizational structure of international war navies.
Additional merits, particularly on uniformed officers, can be recognized with medals. Another section on this deck is dedicated to the close quarters on board, the daily routine on long ocean tours and the often inhumane conditions during wartime. The exhibits show a life at times when survival of the community was only possible through strict discipline.

1 UNIFORMS FROM AROUND THE WORLD

Standardized uniforms in the modern sense only appeared with the formation of standing armies at the end of the 17th century. The cut of the uniform resembled civilian dress, but from 1710 onwards, unique styles and cuts were developed.

In 1758, King George II selected blue and white with gold buttons as the uniform colours for the British Royal Navy. Thus the 'blue jacket' started its triumphant way around the world. It was internationally adopted by practically all navies. Even today, Great Britain's navy has a significant influence in this regard. The crewmembers' uniforms are first and foremost practical. The broad cut, the open neckline, the blue square collar with silk scarf and the round cap of the 'blue jackets' all derive from the days of sailing ships, when it was vitally important that sailors could move freely among the rigging. Also, in the interior of sailing ships, it was so damp due to a lack of heating that evaporation of sweat could only be ensured with a loose cut. Towards the end of the age of steamships, open clothing such as this was also practical for

work in the boiler and engine rooms, or for loading coal.

The loose, striped collar of seamens' uniforms was originally intended to protect the jacket from soiling by hawsers and cables. Even the greased ponytail or 'pigtail' could soil the jacket. Until around 1780, hair was usually worn long, and seamen were required to secure the hair at the back of the head. Some chanced upon the idea of smearing the ponytail with tallow or fat and wrapping it with a tarred hair tie. Until about 1860, seamen and cabin boys were only allowed to wear footwear in winter. Underwear was not standard used in any navy until the mid-19th century.

With later uniforms, the square shape of the collar came into use. This light-blue collar with three white stripes is still symbolic of naval crews.

As for officers' uniforms, no specific dress was required for them until the mid-18th century. They wore high-status civilian dress and decorated it at their own discretion. In 1795, epaulettes were first worn by English officers as rank insignia.

Highlight: Baton of Großadmiral Henning von Holtzendorff – one of only four Großadmiral batons from the German Empire. Two of them are located at the IMMH.

Admiral Kluth, Dress Uniform,
around 1865 Germany, Prussian Navy

Headgear

Naval headgear was once as diverse as
other clothing. Besides headscarves,
felt caps and caps of all kinds, from the
mid-18th century onward, the headgear
of crews consisted of a round hat made
of sailcloth or leather. A coat of tar was
often applied for protection against the
weather.

In the cold seasons, leather hats dressed
with fur were worn, and in summer,
straw hats. Seamen wrapped a blue band
around their hats and caps, upon which
they painted or embroidered the name of
their ship. The modern cap band evolved
from these. According to tradition, the
long band ends are reminiscent of the
pigtails of seamen.

The bicorne hats of officers came about
by turning up the brim on crew members'
round hats. They were worn with the
points towards the front and back. The
English form has high, round folded-up
brims, while the French form has a low,
four-sided shape. The hat is trimmed with
a golden ornament (agraffe). On both
points there are golden or silver tassels,
beneath the ornament, the respective national cockade (a round, stitched-on insignia). The outer edges of admirals' hats often have wide gold trim and are decorated
with black and white ostrich feathers.
Starting around 1800, the more or less
cylindrical shako came to be worn by
sailors. The popularity of the shako results from the constant interaction of
uniform and fashion trends. This cylindrical hat had been a fashion hit in civilian
dress since 1790. Many images from the
romantic period and the Biedermeier period show civilians, seamen and soldiers
with very similarly-styled headdress.
In many navies, cylindrical hats with the
appropriate national emblem continued
to be worn until the mid-19th century.

Some colonial troops also wore helmets with points.

At the end of 1842, Prussia introduced the pickelhaube ('spiked helmet'). Initially, this was also worn by the naval corps. Although the official name for this headgear was simply 'helmet', the name 'Pickelhaube' (a compound of the German words for 'point' or 'pickaxe' and 'cap') quickly took hold. Due to its obvious practical advantages, the pickelhaube was very soon adopted by many countries.

Due to the controversial role of the Prussian army in the defeat of the revolutionary movements of 1848–49, the pickelhaube became a symbol for military and reactionary political forces.

Tarbush for police askaris,
(locally recruited soldiers in Africa)
around 1910 Germany, protection forces

Fez for crews of the SMS 'Goeben' and SMS 'Breslau' in Turkish service,
around 1914, Germany Imperial navy

Steel helmet, around 1960
German Democratic Republic Volksmarine (East German People's Navy)

Fez for crews of Muslim faith,
1913 model, Austria
Approval for wearing the fez in the Austro-Hungarian navy was granted in response to an appeal by a naval cadet from

Highlight:
Fez for crews of Muslim faith
in the Austro-Hungarian Navy

DECK 4

83

Sarajevo. He had explained to Emperor Franz Josef about his imminent disinheritance if he, as a practising Muslim, was not allowed to wear the fez at least part of the time. From that point onward, all navy personnel of Muslim faith were issued the fez as a part of the standard uniform.

2 RITUALS AND CELEBRATIONS AT SEA

To make up for the taxing work of serving at sea, Christian celebrations, equator-crossing ceremonies and other celebrations were held. Pastoral care also had this place on board a ship.

On-board Christmas tree, 1940, Germany
Made by crew members of the heavy cruiser 'Admiral Scheer' for 'Oberleutnant zur See' (Sub Lieutenant) Dietrich Kropp in the south Atlantic.

Photo postcard 'In commemoration of
the wartime Christmas of 1916'
2nd Torpedo Division

'Fressfahrplan' ('Feeding schedule')
POW camp at Trial Bay, Australia, 1916

2 menus
POW camp in Japan, 1917

Certificate of 'baptism on the line'
(equator)
Line-crossing baptism on board SMS 'Arco-
na', 1908

Certificate of wartime emergency baptism
On board SMS 'Kronprinz Wilhelm', 1914

'Neptune'
Costume, training sailing ship

'Gorch Fock', around 1980
Cap, jacket and staff were used both for the
equatorial crossing ceremony as well as in
celebrations of the Feast of St. Nicholas.

Chaplaincy on board

Along with medical personnel, chaplains
are protected under the Geneva Convention. Chaplains served mostly as local
clerics at the navy stations, where the
garrison churches were located. 'Heavenly
pilots' ('Himmelslotsen') were shipped out
to training ships and squadrons and held
church services on Sundays and holidays.
In addition to their clerical activities,
they managed the ship's library, and gave
lectures 'to increase the patriotic spirit
and the historical, geographical and general knowledge'. The war flag was flown
for the duration of the church service,
but above this, the church pennant was
flown. This was the international signal
flag for '8'.
If there was no chaplain on board, church
services were held by an officer. The
deeply religious Großadmiral Raeder was
responsible for the continuation of religious services in the Imperial German
War Navy.

Memorial sheet in remembrance of
Leutnant zur See (~Ensign) Erhard
Fallen on 29 January 1911 in battle against
the revolutionaries in Nanking.

'Wilhelm Gustloff', 1938
In 1945, the cruise ship 'Wilhelm Gustloff',
put into service by the Nazi organization
'Kraft durch Freude' ('Strength through Joy',
abbreviated KdF), met a tragic end. After
the outbreak of the Second World War,
the former KdF ship served as a hospital
and barracks ship until the end of the war,
when it was used as part of 'Operation

The ministry
on board

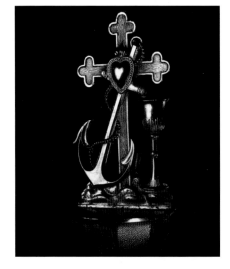

Rescue'. East Prussian civilians and military units fleeing the Soviet Red Army hoped to be evacuated to the West on the 'Gustloff'. Completely overloaded with around 10,000 people, the ship was torpedoed by the Soviet submarine 'S-13' shortly after departure from Gotenhafen (Gdingen, today Gdynia). Only 1,239 passengers and crew survived. This model of the 'Wilhelm Gustloff' at 1:100 scale was given to the International Maritime Museum in March 2010 by the film company UFA and the television company ZDF. It is a floating replica that was used for special effects during the filming of the ZDF two-part series 'Die Gustloff'. Built-in ballast tanks made it possible to reconstruct the sinking of the ship, among other scenes.

3 SHIP PHYSICIANS

The risk of illness on board slow sailing ships was tremendous due to lack of hygiene. An ill crew member often meant death for many others on board, since life in close quarters increased susceptibility to contagious diseases. English and French naval physicians were pioneers in on-board hygiene. In 1805, the English navy was the first to require that naval physicians hold a doctoral degree from a university.
Special requirements were placed on naval physicians. Many countries established special medical colleges for naval physicians. There, field surgery, tropical medicine as well as nautical and tropical hygiene were taught. Medical officers and staff are part of warships' crews to support naval physicians.

General physician Gutschow
Germany, watercolour, around 1910
In 1866, Hermann Gutschow served as an assistant field physician in the Austro-Prussian War and entered the navy after passing the state exam in 1868. After several on-board assignments and temporary duties at the Friedrich Wilhelm Institute and the Charité hospital, he was appointed to establish the navy hospital at Yokohama. In 1884, he returned to Germany. After several command assignments, he first became head of the naval medical corps, then Generalstabsarzt ('Staff-Surgeon General') of the German Navy.

Highlight: Portrait of Hermann Gutschow, the first Generalstabsarzt ('Staff-Surgeon General') of the German Navy.

Stone, bronze, iron, steel – then there was only shooting

Humans reach for weapons during conflicts. Archaeological finds have shown this to be true even among the Neanderthals 36,000 years ago. The earliest weapons used in hand-to-hand combat were hand axes, axes and knives made of stone, wood and bone. Spears, bows and arrows, first used for hunting, allowed people to strike their opponents from greater distances. The development of bronze weapons – copper alloyed with tin – began 5,000 years ago, and bronze swords began to spread about 3,500 years ago. The Iron Age followed, with sharper iron blades that would not bend as easily. Viking swords (around 1,000 AD) had a double-edged blade with a heavy pommel. In the 16th century, epees almost completely replaced previous swords, and the sabre developed from the single-edged sword. They were used in the navy as boarding weapons and were part of the on-board arms of war and merchant ships. During the mid-17th century, weapons for hand-to-hand combat – i.e. weapons for slashing, stabbing and hitting, soon made mostly from steel, that relied upon human strength – became increasingly standardized. Governments have specified models and patterns upon which the production of blades was to be based. Such weapons became primarily showpieces and are still used in many navies around the world as officer decorations. Bows and arrows, knives, spears and swords were the primary fighting weapons for about 10,000 years. Around 500 years passed between the invention of firearms and the development of machine guns. Then it was only another 40 years before the invention of the nuclear bomb as a weapon of mass destruction.

Hand axe
c. 8.000–6,000 BC, obsidian

'Ear' sword
c. 1000 BC

Austria
Admiral's sabre, around 1800

Russia, Curved officer's sabre, around 1820

Viking sword
8th–10th century
Until about the year 1100, swords in most of Europe had the general form of a Viking sword. It had a double-edged blade with a short cross guard and a heavy pommel. Since the 12th and 13th centuries, the blade has been more tapered towards the tip so that it could be used for thrusting as well as slashing.

> **Highlight:**
> **Viking sword** – a very rare, early example with a pattern-welded blade.

Officer's dagger,
1849 model, Imperial German Navy
Admiral Hugo von Pohl first used this dagger as a naval cadet. Starting in 1873, however, officers on general duty carried only sabres. We can assume that Admiral von Pohl resumed the use of his cadet's sidearm with the reintroduction of the dagger in 1901.

USA
Honorary epee of Captain Gustavas Cunningham, 4 July 1804. Gift by the Pennsylvania state assembly for his service to the American people.

German Democratic Republic, People's Navy, admiral's dagger, around 1975. The dagger, introduced in 1961 for male officers and admirals, was worn as a part of the dress uniform, full dress uniform and ceremonial uniform.

Germany
Hanse dagger, 16th century

French boarding axe, around 1860

Lunten-Faustrohr ('Lunten fist pipe') beginning of 16th century

France, percussion pistol, 1837 model, first version

Denmark navy revolver, 1871 model

Spain Carbine '98K' with rifle grenade device
Year of manufacture: 1944

Soviet Union Makarov pistol, around 1970

3-pound chain-shot, end of 16th century
Chainshot was used to attack the sails and rigging of enemy ships.

12-pound iron shot, 18th century

History in miniature format

Sculpted miniature figures have been made since the early history of humanity. Tin figures were manufactured as toys for children until the beginning of the 20th century. Tin, lead and elastolin were used as materials, and today, synthetic resins.

In earlier times, painting of the figures was done mostly at home by women and children. Today the flat or full figures are either painted in factories or are plain and then carefully painted by collectors.

Pinnace, painted tin flat figure

Development of naval artillery, 18th–20th centuries

From the middle of the 14th century, light cannons were introduced onto ship decks in Europe. Naval artillery did not become the main weapon on sailing warships until the second half of the 16th century. Very little changed until the beginning of the age of the steamship. The average shot distance amounted to approximately 600 m. Rear-loading guns made of drawn steel with long-range ammunition were first introduced in 1850 which increased both range and fire power. During World War I, the range was around 18 km. In the Second World War, the ranges increased to a maximum of 35 km. Today, warships have rapid-fire weapons with diameters of 40 to 127 mm, missiles with ranges of up to 300 km, anti-submarine torpedo guns, depth charges and minelaying equipment.

Stone shot, mid-15th century

5 LIFE ON BOARD

Duties and daily routine

At the end of the 19th century, active service for young men began on the ir 18th birthday and lasted for three years in most navies. After that, men belonged to the reserve for four years, and then served in the Sea Defence or in the 'Reinforcement Reserve'. In February and October, new recruits were sworn in. After uniforms were issued, the greater part of training took place on board, where initial infantry training was held. Then there was training in boat service, in weapons exercises and other on-board duties. Particularly suitable recruits also received special training. Frequent sailing exercises at sea intensified and extended their training.

The first officer was responsible for the allocation and scheduling of daily duties and leisure time. In the so-called 'routine', the duty roster was set and divided into two main parts – division duty, which comprised all military duties, and 'housekeeping' activities to keep the vessel shipshape.

Zeugflicken.

Postcard

Similar training courses were carried out on the ships of most navies around the world, and have been continued in many regards up until the present day.

Commemorative and reservist pieces

A hundred years ago, the words 'leisure time' and 'holiday' still sounded strange. Journeymen and merchants had to travel for work, and sailors saw foreign harbours, but the majority of people spent most of their lives in their local community. Military service was thus a welcome opportunity for many young men to break free

Commemorative plate, around 1990, Turkey

of the restrictions of home. If there was a chance to serve on a navy ship or to travel to distant colonies at the state's expense, many volunteers answered the call.

Daily routine of seamen on board a German warship at port, around 1900:

4:20 AM Inspection of the night watch, half of the watch fetch water for cleaning. Late sleepers were pitched from their hammocks with the 'sergeant's grip'.

4:50 AM Wake-up call for the boatswain, gunmaster and their mates, as well as the security watch.

5:00 AM Overall wake-up call by the boatswain.

5:05 AM 'Gather hammocks', 'Up all hammocks'. With these commands, the hammocks, which had already been tied together by the crew, were stowed in the hammock chests on deck.

5:10 AM 'Wash up' and dress in the day's uniform, as previously ordered.

5:30 AM Pipes and matches out (no more smoking).

5:40 AM 'Clean ship'. In summer, this was done barefoot, and on Saturdays the deck was scrubbed even more thoroughly.

6.40 AM Wake-up of the ensigns and stowage of their hammocks.

6:50 AM 'Backen und Banken' (set the tables and benches for mealtime). For mealtimes, tables and benches on the gun deck and berth deck were folded out in order to take breakfast – consisting of coffee, bread and butter – at 7:00 AM. The coffee was fetched from the galley in large kettles by the 'Backschafter' (busser). Butter was set in the middle of the table for shared use. Every man received a loaf of darkbread every four days and rationed it by himself.

7:20 AM Relieve posts.

7:30 AM Sick into the sick bay.

7:35 AM Pipes and matches out (no more smoking).

7.40 AM Clear the decks, clean the brass.

7:45 AM Change of watch.

7:55 AM Prepare for flag ceremony.

8:00 AM Raising of flag on upper deck.

'During the flag ceremony, as the war flag is raised or lowered, deck officers, non-commissioned officers and crew are to stand still on the upper deck, facing the flag; officers shall salute with their hand at their headgear'.

8:10 AM Clean artillery.

8:45 AM Clean handguns.

9:00 AM Prepare for inspection.

9:10 AM Inspection, i.e. 'muster'.

9:30 AM Begin service. Division duty consisted of weapons drills, instruction, exercise and frequently on ships with rigging, sailing exercises.

11:30 AM Prepare deck, meaning that the deck would be cleared, swept and cleaned.

11:45 AM 'Backen und Banken' (Take places for mealtime).

12:00 PM All men to lunch.
While the menu at port was more varied, ingredients at sea repeated in a cycle such as the following:

Monday	– Peas
Tuesday	– Beans
Wednesday	– Plums
Thursday	– Rice
Friday	– Peas
Saturday	– Beans
Sunday	– Plums

12:30 PM Relieve posts, wash dishes.

1:00 PM Meal crews receive provisions.

1:45 PM Pipes and matches out, sweep deck.

2:00 PM Division duties or uniform inspections, lessons, shooting and similar.

4:00 PM Clear deck and short break.

4:30 PM Back to work.

5:30 PM Workday finished, final deck preparations, hoist boats, cover guns etc., leave granted.

5:50 PM Mealtime.

6 PM Dinner.

It consisted of sweetened tea and buttered bread. If this was insufficient, sailors could purchase sausage, ham or bacon and also pickled herring and gherkins.

6:20 PM Relieve posts. Off-duty present themselves for inspection.

The off-duty personnel then went ashore with the 'routine boat'. Music could be played at this time.

7:30 PM Clean and sweep lower decks. Pipes and matches out (no more smoking) below deck.

7:45 PM Main inspection round.

7:50 PM Present hammocks for inspection by the boatswain.

8:00 PM Inspection of the night watch and allocation of watches.

9:00 PM Curfew,

Quiet on the ship, rounds (tour of the ship to inspect the watches).

10:00 PM Lights out in the deck officers' mess.

11:00 PM Lights out in the officers' mess.

On Saturdays from 4:00 AM to noon the deck was scrubbed, in the afternoon weapons and gunnery were cleaned. Work finished at 4:00 PM.

On Sundays, morning washing of decks and cleaning of artillery was also performed, but to a lesser extent.
At 10:00 AM the crew was inspected by the commanders, and then the chaplain held church services. If there was no chaplain on board, the commander or an

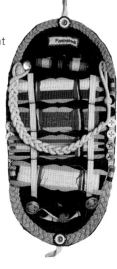

Sewing kit,
around 1910
Imperial German Navy

Highlight: the painting 'Gewehrreinigen im Batteriedeck eines Großkampfschiffes' ('Cleaning of Guns on the Gundeck of a Capital Ship') is one of the few images documenting the life of the crews.

'Gewehrreinigen im Batteriedeck eines Großkampfschiffes' ('Cleaning of Guns on the Gundeck of a Capital Ship')
Hans Meerkor
Oil on canvas, around 1875

officer appointed by him read a text aloud from the prayer book. After the noon meal, crew members generally looked for a suitable place to take a nap on deck.

At 1:30 PM the men could go ashore, and the return transport of sailors on Sunday leave was at 10:00 PM, 11:00 PM, or midnight. After the first shorter training journeys came longer ones. Generally, three of these voyages were made – one each in spring, summer and autumn. In winter, the ships were usually in the shipyards for repairs and maintenance.

At the end of the year, the crew was given Christmas and New Year's leave in shifts. In order to check the training status of the crews, inspections were held from time to time. The most important of these took place twice per year and involved all divisions. Junior officers were also subject to an inspection of sailing exercises and manoeuvring on their own ship as well as crew command exercises. In September of each year, the main exercise of the active battle fleet was held.

This was the keystone in the training of new recruits. At the end of September, reservists were released to return home. In addition to ships' crews, there were naval divisions on land such as auxiliary seamen divisions, shipyard units, torpedo divisions and naval gunmen. There were also incredible numbers of crews at onshore posts. There they served as batmen, writers, orderlies, telegraphists, printers, signalmen at coastal stations, at pigeon postal service stations, at shipyards and other naval installations.

'Essenprobe' ('Meal tasting') From: 'Unsere Marine' ('Our Navy') C.W. Allers

Examples of annual salaries in the Imperial German Navy around 1900:

Ship boys (Schiffsjungen):	144 marks
Able seamen (Obermatrosen):	288 marks
Petty officers (Maate):	450 marks
Deck officers (Deckoffiziere):	1,692 gold marks
Junior lieutenants (Leutnante):	900 gold marks
Lieutenants (Kapitänleutnante):	3,900 gold marks
Captains (Kapitäne zur See):	7,800 gold marks
Admirals, vice admirals and rear admirals:	12,000 gold marks

Grand Admiral von Tirpitz, as the highest ranking officer of the navy, received 30,000 gold marks annually and a free official residence.

Around 1910, daily sea rations for crews provided the following numbers of total calories:

Argentina:	3,745
Brazil:	3,899
Germany:	4,082
France:	2,356
Great Britain:	3,988
Italy:	2,914
Japan:	4,381
Mexico:	4,589
Norway:	4,499
Austria-Hungary:	3,170
Russia:	3,986
Sweden:	4,401
Turkey:	3,986
United States:	5,197

Musicians and bandsmen

Navy bands have a tradition of more than five hundred years. Their instrumentation corresponded to what was called for in infantry bands brass, woodwinds, percussion and Turkish crescent. They were stationed at all major navy bases.

Installation
'Officer's cabin'

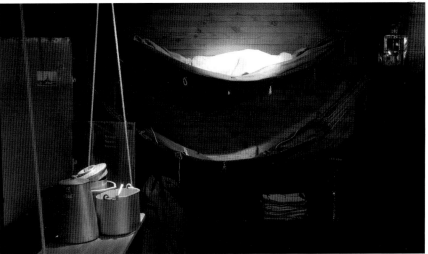

Installation
'Crew cabin'

Today the instrumentation and repertoire are flexible and versatile. In addition to musical accompaniment of military ceremonies, concerts, musical shows and galas as well as jazz, chamber and dance music are all performed by navy bands.

On larger ships, there often existed an on-board band. The musicians were recruited from among the crew.

Whistles, bugles and drums were mainly used to give commands, but could also accompany salutes and parade marches.

6 STUDY COLLECTION OF MEDALS AND BADGES OF HONOUR

'What is a medal? A cost-saving object that allows the satisfaction of a great deal of vanity with a small piece of metal'. Aristide Briand (1862–1932), French statesman and winner of the Nobel Peace Prize

Every community has a certain need to give and receive recognition, praise and reward. Honourees are recognized by the community by means of visible decorations – even if symbols such as medals and badges of honour are not undisputed in public opinion. Under the absolutist feudal systems of the 17th and 18th centuries, court and house medals were awarded only to members of the nobility. In the 19th century, societies became more open, and the middle classes boomed. The rulers in every country accordingly devised a category of decorations in the form of crosses and medals, in addition to the previous classes of medals. These were intended for all levels of society. Even today, decorations of honour very tangibly reflect the societal development of states and their international relations.

Großadmiral Hans von Koester

Born on April 29, 1844 in the town of Schwerin, he entered the Prussian Navy in 1854 already and was appointed instructor at the naval academy in 1875. When he assumed his role as head of the training command, he began his career as a training ship and fleet commander. In 1892, he was promoted to the rank of Vice Admiral, on March 22, 1897 to that of Admiral and was made 'Großadmiral' on June 28, 1905. Koester was a sailor and soldier through and through, coming as he did from the

times of sailing ships. As 'Exerziermeister der Flotte' ('Training Master of the Fleet') he played a vital role in the training of artillery and manoeuvring capabilities within the fleet. He died in Kiel on February 21, 1928.

Gift of honour to the Head of the Imperial Admiralty Albrecht von Stosch, 1885

Given by 'German industrialists'. Design and execution by Prof. Adolf Schill, produced in collaboration with leading sculptors, artistic craftsmen and historians of the period. Albrecht von Stosch (1818–1896) was appointed officer in the Prussian Army in 1835 and after various assignments was promoted to Head of the Imperial Admiralty in 1872. His greatest contribution is considered to be the improvement of German shipbuilding.

**Design drawing of the gift of honour
to the Head of the Imperial Admiralty
Albrecht von Stosch,** 1885.
Signed: 'Adolf Schill drafted Puseldorf
1883'. Gouache on paper

**Standards: of His Majesty the Kaiser, of
Her Majesty the Kaiserin, of the Royal Court and of the Imperial Prussian
Princes**
These standards are extremly rare relics
of the Imperial German Navy. They were
flown from the top of the main mast if
royalty boarded a warship. If a ship with
a raised standard of this type approached
other ships at anchor, the crews were sent
up to the yards to greet the royal visitor
with a shout of 'Their Majesties', three
shouts of 'Hurrah' and the waving of caps.
The marine guards presented their arms,
and the drummers played a march. More-
over, each ship fired a salute. The Kaiser
was saluted with 33 cannon shots, and
other royalty was saluted with 21 shots.

**Standard
of the German Kaiserin,**
around 1900

**Standard of the Imperial
Prussian**
House, around 1900

**Standard of the Imperial
Prussian Princes,**
around 1910

HIGHLIGHTS ON DECK 5

Model of the paddle steamer 'Barbarossa'
This ship was part of the German Federal fleet, which was formed after the Revolution of 1848.

Model of the USS 'Monitor'
This ironclad ship built in 1862 had a revolving gun turret midships, a revolution in naval ship design.

Model of the HMS 'Ariel'
This destroyer was one of the first ships with gearbox turbines.

'Royal Navy 1896 – Our First Line of Defence', news-paper supplement on the importance of the British Navy at the climax of its power.

'U 53' stellt den norwegischen Segler 'Asheim' ('U 53' scuttles the Norwegian sailing ship 'Asheim'): submarine warfare according to prize rules, in a water-colour by Claus Bergen, 1917.

'H.L. Hunley', this submersible was in 1864 the first of its type to sink a ship during wartime.

Leather uniform from 'U 96'
Extra leather clothing of the commanding officer of 'U 96' of 1941 – 40 years later known around the world as Lothar-Günther Buchheim's 'Das Boot'.

Model of the battleship 'Bismarck'
Today still a legendary ship due to its unusual fate.

The 'Yamato', Japanese battleship, equipped with the heaviest guns ever to be mounted on a ship.

Ejection seat made by the company Martin-Baker – life insurance for pilots.

WAR AND PEACE: NAVIES OF THE WORLD SINCE 1815

The exhibits on Deck 5 present the evolution of the naval forces in the 19th and 20th centuries.

The industrial revolution of the 19th century also affected warship construction: sails were no longer used for ship propulsion, but rather steam engines, followed by turbines and oil and diesel engines. At the same time, armour protection of hulls was in constant competition with the development of shells, guns and finally long-range guided weapons. The advent of mines and torpedoes as well as the development of a new, incredible weapon, the submarine, further increased potential threats. Strategy and tactics in naval warfare adapted to each leap in development.

Capital ships were symbols of national power and the technical and industrial capability of a state. Seapower was measured primarily by the number of capital ships. Arms races followed, but submarines and airplanes in the Second World War brought an end to the dominance of the battleship. During and especially after the end of the Cold War, another far-reaching change in strategy took place. Submarine fleets and aircraft carriers armed with nuclear weap-

ons dominated the strategies and actions of the naval powers. Today, new threat scenarios such as international terrorism call for novel solutions, including a new kind of naval defence.

1 MILITARY EXPERIMENTS, 1815–1865

The German Federal Navy: the navy of two revolutions, 1848–1852

On 14 June 1848, the Frankfurt National Assembly passed a resolution to establish a German national navy. The immediate motivation for this was the Danish blockade of the German coasts in the conflict over the duchies Sleswig and Holstein. After all, this navy was the result of two revolutions – one social and one technologial. The decision to establish a navy was based on a political and revolutionary movement which finally lead to a German parliament. Concerning the technological aspects, the National Assembly planned to acquire a fleet of steamships. This was a very modern concept for the time that involved fundamental innovations in the organizational structure of the navy. In the summer of 1849, the attempt to establish a democratic nation state in

Germany failed. This failure also meant the end of the German Federal fleet. In 1852 its remnants were auctioned off.

'Barbarossa'

Steam frigate, Federal navy, Germany
The ship's eponym, Kaiser Friedrich I Barbarossa, symbolized the pursuit of a strong and unified empire – very much like the aspirations of the German revolutionaries of 1848. On June 1849, the 'Barbarossa' of the Federal Navy took part in the fleet encounter off Heligoland. 1:40 scale, model maker: Bruno Kramp

Technological innovations in the Crimean War and the American Civil War

In the mid 19th c., the Industrial Revolution lead to radical innovations in the navies of Western Europe as well as the USA. The wooden sailing ships of the line were ousted by steam-powered, screw-driven iron-armoured ships; solid projectiles were replaced by high-explosive shells. During the Crimean War (1854-56) for the first time, ships armoured with iron were operating as 'floating batteries' bombarding the coast. The tactical superiority of propulsion with steam and screw compared to sail was evident in the western powers' total control of the Baltic and the Black Sea. Russia, as

Highlight:
Model of the paddle steamer 'Barbarossa'
This ship was part of the German Federal Navy, which was established during the Revolution of 1848.

the inferior power at sea, saw her chance in a new weapon: stationary sea mines with unforeseeable destructive power.

During the American Civil War (1861–65), two iron-armoured warships ('ironclads') clashed for the first time. Revolving gun turrets and the submarine confronted the navies of the world with entirely new challenges. Nothing remained of the sailing battlefleet of the time of Admiral Horatio Nelson.

'Monitor'
Ironcald warship, U.S. Navy, USA
Designed by the Swedish engineer and inventor John Ericsson in 1861, the 'Monitor' was intended for operations in shallow coastal waters. With its low freeboard and practically non-existent superstructure, the underlying principle of its design was to reduce its exposure to attack as much as possible. Its main feature was its revolving gun turret, a revolution in naval ship design.
1:96 scale, model maker: Freerk de Vries

Battle of Hampton Roads
The engagement between the 'Monitor' of the Union navy and the 'Virginia' of the Confederate navy was the first encounter between ironclad warships. The fighting lasted for several hours, but neither ship could deal the decisive blow even at point-blank range. Many times the 'Monitor' manouvered so close to its opponent that 'Virginia' couldn't bring any gun to bear on her. Because of its shallow draft the Union ship was very versatile and evaded several attempts by the 'Virginia' to ram her.

'Virginia' (ex 'Merrimack')
Ironclad warship, Confederate Navy, CSA
The 'Virginia' was the world's first fully iron-armoured ship to be powered by steam engines and propellers – a so-called 'ironclad'. The 'Virginia' was rebuilt from a sailing frigate whose upper decks and masts were removed. 1:150 scale, model maker: Sidney Wolvek

Highlight: Model of USS 'Monitor' – This ironclad ship built in 1862 had a midship revolving gun turret, a revolution in naval shipbuilding.

27.9 cm Dahlgren gun in a turret, U.S. Navy, USA, 1862
This bottleneck-shaped, cast-iron muzzle-loading gun was named after its designer, Rear Admiral John Dahlgren. Because of its special shape, the force of the expand-

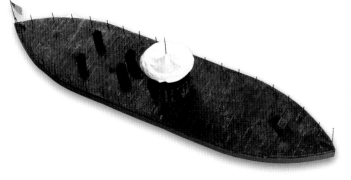

ing propellant gases could be distributed in order to protect the gun barrel from bursting. Dahlgren guns could be mounted in revolving turrets. This type of mount was used on most monitor-type ships in the Union Navy, including the 'monitor' itself, as well as on the subsequent classes 'Neosho', 'Marietta', 'Casco' and 'Milwaukee'.
1:32 scale, model maker: Olaf Krabbenhöft

2 TORPEDOES AGAINST IRONCLAD WARSHIPS

New technology in the 'Era of Uncertainty' (1861–1890)

The stormy technological development led to considerable innovations in the construction of large battleships by the mid 19th c. The navies were in search for the optimal constructive joining of propulsion, armament, and armour. In France, the naval school of thought 'Jeune École' developed an alternative to the traditional exertion of sea power with ironclads. The strategic objective was to challenge the security of the British Empire, France's traditional rival at sea.

After defeat in the Franco-Prussian War in 1870–1871, it was no longer possible for France to finance the construction of large ironclad warships to compete with Britain. Proposals to abandon battle fleet dogma in favour of other strategies gained traction. For this, new technological advances made for more inexpensive naval forces: the oceangoing torpedo boat and the fast, armed cruiser. This strategy gained acceptance in Europe and the USA.

HMS 'Sans Pareil'

Battleship, Royal Navy, Great Britain
In spite of its name, HMS 'Sans Pareil' was still a typical product of the 'Era of Uncertainty' – it had an armament consisting of all types of calibre common at that time. Servicing the various gun types and storing many types of ammunition presented serious problems. This waterline model shows the livery of the 'Victorian Navy' around 1890. 1:100 scale.

'Duilio'

Ironclad warship, Regia Marina, Italy
In the international arms race, Italy relied on a small number of ironclad warships that were meant to prevail with fighting strength and steadfastness. Following this strategy, the 'Duilio' possessed the heaviest muzzle-loading armament ever

to be installed on a warship. Its diameter was 45 cm.
1:100 scale, model maker: Jürgen Eichardt

'A 19'

Torpedo boat, Imperial Navy, Germany
Intended for use as a torpedo and mine-searching boat. During the First World War the torpedo boat and minesweeper 'A 19' served as flotilla-leader of the Flanders mine-sweeping half-flotilla. On March 21st 1918, the boat was rammed and sunk by the British destroyer HMS 'Botha'.
1:100 scale, model maker: Anton Happach

HMS 'Ariel'

Torpedo boat destroyer, Royal Navy, Great Britain
At the request of the Admiralty for the 'greatest possible speed', the 'Ariel' was one of the first ships to be equipped with gearbox turbines. It was able to reach up to 31 knots. 1:48 scale

'Torpedoboote ran an den Feind' ('Torpedo boats, let's go get 'em!')

Willy Stöwer (1864–1931),
Oil on canvas, 1913
In rough seas, a torpedo boat breaks through the line of the ironclads. In the masthead the red swallowtailed pennant 'Z', the signal for 'Ran an den Feind', can be seen. Willy Stöwer's 1913 dramatic imagery captures an exercise of the Imperial German Navy. One year later, during the First World War, the 'Jeune Ècole's' school of thought - torpedo boat vs. ironclad – became reality.

3 COLONIALISM AND NAVIES

Carving up the world – Great Powers scramble for overseas colonies

There was a global change in the structure of colonial empires at the end of the 19th c. The oldest colonial powers, Spain and Portugal, had lost their possessions in Central and South America. Britain became the greatest colonial power and soon held sway over a quarter of the world's land surface. Africa was almost entirely divided among the European powers. The USA asserted her sole claim to the American continent with the Monroe Doctrine.

The German Empire became involved in the race for overseas possessions only at a late stage, acquiring colonies and 'protectorates' in Africa, Oceania and China. It was about securing a 'place in the sun' (Foreign Secretary Bernhard von Bülow) alongside other European powers. Colonialism during the Age of Imperialism involved formal – often violent – annexation of territory (as in Africa) as well as exertion of economic influence (by leases). The naval forces engaged in the protection of sea trade as well as the acquisition of colonies and their protection against competing colonial powers and natives' rebellions. Fleet units were also often deployed to protect life and property of the colonists.

Display case: colonial presence in China

This display case is primarily dedicated to the German colonial presence in East Asia, particularly in China since 1897. A 1:50 scale model of the gunboat 'Iltis' of the Imperial German Navy is displayed, which was part of the international naval forces at the battle of 'Taku Forts' in 1900, during the Boxer Rebellion.

The special supplement to the 'Berliner Lokal-Anzeiger' on 2 July 1900 reports on the assassination of the German ambassador to China in Beijing by protesters in the Boxer social movement, correctly called the 'Movement of the Society for Righteousness and Harmony'. Six European powers as well as the USA and Japan sent ships and troops to defeat the subsequent Chinese uprising against the foreign powers.

The proclamation on the occupation of Kiautschou on 14 November 1897 by Rear Admiral Diederichs, Commander of the East Asian Cruiser Squadron, marked the beginning of German military intervention in China. The operation was not, as assumed at the time, a spontaneous reaction to the murder of two German missionaries, but rather an operation that had been carefully planned for quite some time.

Display case – colonial period

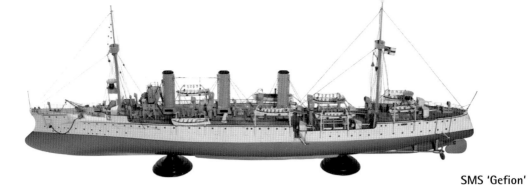

SMS 'Gefion'

'Graf Goetzen', 1915

Built in 1913 at the Meyer shipyard in Papenburg for service on Lake Tanganyika, the ship was first disassembled into its individual components. It was then delivered by train and steamship in 5,000 wooden crates to its destination in the German colony of German East Africa. Under the leadership of three expert shipbuilders who had travelled with the disassembled ship, 250 natives and 20 Indians reassembled the steamship. Put into service in February 1915, it was used as a gunboat, troop transport, as well as a cargo and passenger transport.
1:100 scale

SMS 'Oldenburg', 1884

Ironclad corvette, Imperial German Navy, Germany
The history of the ironclad corvette SMS 'Oldenburg' is one involving a series of unfortunate events. On three occasions, applications were made to include its construction in the navy budget – each time in vain. The Reichstag didn't approve it until the fourth time, and only with immense financial cuts. What resulted was a trimmed-down version of the 'Sachsen' class that was hardly fit for its intended use. As the last German capital ship, the artillery of the 'Oldenburg' was mounted in so-called casemates, fortified gun emplacements embedded in the hull. Other navies had long since gone to turrets on the main deck. Useless to the navy, and hardly impressive when when showing the flag in foreign waters, the 'Oldenburg' brought zero return on a meagre investment. Still, the 79-metre-long ship was the first to be built completely from domestically produced steel. 1:100 scale, model maker: Günther Seherr

SMS 'Gefion'

Cruiser corvette, Imperial Navy, Germany
The cruiser corvette SMS 'Gefion' was built as a fleet escort and ship for foreign deployment. As such it was the forerunner of the later small cruisers of the Imperial navy. Due to poorly executed construction and insufficiently ventilated engine rooms, the ship proved to be a a a failed design for foreign missions. The 'Gefion' was attached to the East Asiatic Cruiser Division only from 1897 to 1901. A landing corps from the 'Gefion' took part in the failed Seymour Expedition (Boxer Rebellion) in June 1900. From 1901 to 1904 it underwent a complete overhaul in Germany, then it was put into naval reserve. Rebuilt as motorship 'Adolf Sommerfeld' in 1920, the former 'Gefion' served civilian purposes until it was scrapped in 1923.
1:100 scale

4 THE ERA OF UNCERTAINTY

The pre-dreadnought battleship in the industrial age. Expansion of fleets worldwide

In the 1880s, various countries developed so-called 'Pre-Dreadnought' battleships. The armament with two gun turrets forward and aft on deck, the quality of the armour-plating material, and propulsion technology had reached a technical level permitting standardisation of ship building. The one exception was the wide range of the armament calibre on board. Now, the quantitative expansion of the fleet became more important than technical innovation. A country's sea power was measurable by the number of her ironclads and cruisers, and this in turn became the basis for the famous German 'Naval Laws'.
The theoretical basis for this development was provided by Alfred Thayer Mahan's 'The Influence of Sea Power upon History' (1890) - a work on global strategy and tactics. This was also the beginning of the Age of Imperialism and the colonial expansion of the European countries and the USA,

101

inevitably leading to armed conflicts. The first major engagement between ironclad fleets took place between the Japan and Russia at Tsushima in 1905. Reports on the event provoked worldwide attention, a foreboding of the destructive powers of the modern fleets.

SMS 'Radetzky'
Battleship, Austro-Hungarian Navy
The battleships of the 'Radetzky'-class battleships were the first pre-dreadnought battleships built by Austria-Hungary that met contemporary standards. Immediately after the namesake ship was commissioned, the 'Radetzky' took part in the Coronation Fleet Review on 24 June 1911 before King George V in Spithead, England.
1:100 scale, model maker: Miroslav Tesar

SMS 'Medusa'
Small cruiser, Imperial Navy, Germany
Building the small cruiser took ten and a half months. After its trial runs, the ship was placed on reserve for nearly two years due to personnel shortages. Afterwards, the 'Medusa' took part in voyages and manoeuvres of the fleet.
1:50 scale

Uniform of Kaiser Wilhelm II.
as Grand Admiral
Imperial Navy, Germany, around 1902

Uniform of Grand Admiral
Prince Henry of Prussia
Imperial Navy, Germany, around 1914

Display case: Kaiser Wilhelm II.
Kaiser Wilhelm II is considered to be one of the main promoters – and propagandists – for the construction of a German fleet. Next to his figurine the display case shows

Display case 'Yacht Hohenzollern'
This display case is devoted to two significant 'members' of the former imperial family: Grand Admiral Prince Henry of Prussia, brother of Kaiser Wilhelm II., and the yacht 'Hohenzollern'. The imperial yacht was commissioned by Wilhelm II and used for holiday voyages and royal visits (1:100 scale, model maker: Günther Seherr). The Grand Admiral's baton together with the interim version of the Grand Admiral's baton of Prince Henry of Prussia were insignia of imperial might as well as military power. Besides the Kaiser and Admiral Hans von Koester Prince Henry was the third officer of the Imperial Navy bearing the rank of Grand Admiral. The 'interim baton' was intended for everyday use and equipped with an integrated telescope.

Portrait of Kaiser Wilhelm II
The figurine of Kaiser Wilhelm II in front of one of his famous navy lists

a pencil drawing of a 'Battleship off Heligoland' made by the Kaiser in 1893 together with one of his famous navy lists. These allowed for the German fleet - always looked upon by the Kaiser as of inferior quality - to be compared with the naval capabilities of the great powers. This exhibit is a reproduction; property of the von Rehdigersche Stadtbibliothek Breslau.

'Royal Navy 1896 – Our First Line of Defence'

Supplement from: The Graphic, 22/2/1896
After the end of the Napoleonic Wars, Great Britain rose to become the most powerful naval power. Its island location and numerous overseas colonies necessitated a large fleet; the Royal Navy guaranteed the security of the Empire.

Display case: the Battle of Tsushima, 1905
Tsushima, 1905
The emerging powers of Japan and Russia had competed since the end of the 19th century to control parts of the Far East. In January 1904, the Japanese navy attacked the Russian base at Port Arthur; only after a long siege did the Russians surrender. On May 14th 1905 the rest of the Pacific fleet as well as the Russian Baltic fleet encountered a technically and numerically superior Japanese fleet in Tsushima straits.
Amongst other exhibits the display case shows a cardboard model of the Russian protected cruiser 'Askold' (scale 1:150, model maker: M. Rehorst). 'Askold' took part in the 'Battle of the Yellow Sea' in August 1904, where it was heavily damaged. It had to enter the neutral port of Shanghai. Her crew was interned there.

Highlight: 'Royal Navy 1896 – Our First Line of Defence', newspaper supplement on the importance of the British Navy at the height of its power.

DECK 5

103

5 REVOLUTIONS IN EUROPE

Russia 1905, 1917 and the Kiel mutiny of 1918

In 1905, Russia was overshadowed by defeat in the Russo-Japanese war, an economic recession and demands for social reforms, leading to mass strikes and uprisings by peasants and workers. The crew of the 'Potemkin' of the Black Sea fleet mutinied – an event immortalised by the film of the same name by Sergej Eisenstein. Twelve years later, in October 1917, a shot fired by the cruiser 'Aurora' in St. Petersburg gave the signal to revolution. The Bolshevists assumed power in Russia; the 'Ghost of Communism' (Karl Marx) entered the stage of world politics.

In 1918, despite initial negotiations for an armistice, the German Naval Command planned a last honourable foray against the superior Royal Navy. The futility of this undertaking, inactivity for months on end, poor diet and social tensions sparked a mutiny on the large battleships of the German High Seas Fleet in November 1918. The sailors' mutiny spread like wildfire throughout the country. Workers' and soldiers' councils were established according to the Soviet model though leaning more towards social democracy. In this way, the fleet, the 'Kaiser's pride', was instrumental in bringing about the end of the monarchy in Germany.

'Potemkin'

Battleship, Imperial Navy, Russia
The 'Kniaz Potemkin Tavricheskiy', put into service in 1903 gained worldwide attention through the film 'Battleship Potemkin' by Soviet director Sergej Eisenstein. With striking images, the film depicts the events of the mutiny in Odessa in 1905.
Scale 1:100,
model maker: Helmut Schwarzer

Demands of the Soldiers' Council of the High Seas Fleet

Germany, November 9th 1918
Source: Marinemuseum Wilhelmshaven

Seaman of SMS 'Thüringen' with red brassard and red flag, Germany 1918

6 RIVER FLEETS

In this exhibit area you will find ships and boats of European river flotillas, such as the Austro-Hungarian Danube flotilla, of the 19th and 20th centuries.

7 THE 'DREADNOUGHT' ERA

In Great Britain, the First Sea Lord, Sir John Fisher, introduced a fundamental rationalisation of British naval supremacy from 1904. Due to the serious financial crisis in Britain after the expensive Boer War in South Africa (1901), he concentrated on a revolutionary design: a new all-big-gun ship with superior speed, long-range heavy artillery of standard calibre, and precise range measuring. HMS 'Dreadnought' was launched in February 1906 and became the prototype of the battleships of the 20th c. In Germany, Admiral Alfred von Tirpitz realised the plans of Wilhelm II to establish the industrially emerging German Empire as a major sea power. Even the 'most powerful opponent at sea' ought to recognise the risk of defeat in case of a military conflict ('risk fleet'). Since 1898 the German Navy was expanded according to the 'Naval laws', despite strong opposition in the German parliament, the 'Reichstag'. Germany followed with its own 'Dreadnought-leap'. The years up to the First World War in 1914 were overshadowed by a naval arms race between Germany and Britain, with the latter winning. Several 'Dreadnought' races began all over the world: between the Austro-Hungarian Empire and Italy; between Argentina, Brazil, and Chile, while the USA, Japan, Russia, and France also built new 'Dreadnoughts'.

USS 'Michigan'
The drafts for this first American battleship of the dreadnought-type were made even before those of the British ship 'Dreadnought'. Since the latter was completed earlier, it became the namesake of the new ship type. The model shows USS 'Michigan' as it looked in 1916.
1:100 scale, model maker: Werner Schleith

SMS 'Goeben'
Large cruiser, Imperial Navy, Germany Entering service in 1912 and assigned to the Mediterranean Division, 'Goeben' sailed under the Ottoman flag since August 1914. Renamed 'Yavuz Sultan Selim' she fought in the Black Sea against the Russian fleet.

1:100 scale, model construction: G. Schiwek; Collection of Prof. Schneekluth

USS 'Michigan' (above)
SMS 'Goeben' (below)

Gala uniform of Grand Admiral Alfred von Tirpitz,
Imperial Navy, Germany, around 1912 Admiral Alred von Tirpitz, State Secretary in the Imperial Naval Office from 1897 onwards, built up the German Navy in the 19 years that followed. The five Naval laws resp. Naval amendments that he conceived and that won the backing of the Reichstag served as a basis for this development.

8 WEAPONS AT SEA

From round shot to missiles

For nearly 400 years, bronze and iron cannons almost exclusively shot balls. With the introduction of explosive projectiles – first hollow spheres with fuses, then artillery grenades – naval architecture responded with hulls made of iron and steel.

Starting with the Crimean War (1853–56), the naval mine came as a new weapon which necessitated the development of mine defence. Contact mines and remotely controlled mines were used en masse for defensive and offensive minefields.

The modern torpedo, a self-propelled explosive underwater weapon, traces back to the 'fish torpedo', first introduced by Robert Whitehead in 1866. This new weapon soon presented a serious danger for all types of maritime travel. After 1945, intelligent missiles came into use for attacks on targets at sea, on land and in the air. Naval weapons today include mid- to low-calibre radar-guided artillery as well as modern mine and submarine defence weapons.

SMS 'Albatross'

Minelaying cruiser, Imperial German Navy
During the First World War, the 'Albatross'

Highlight: ' "U 53" stellt den norwegischen Segler "Asheim" ' (' "U 53" hunting down the Norwegian sailing ship "Asheim" '): submarine warfare according to prize rules in a watercolour by Claus Bergen, 1917.

laid minefields with up to 350 mines in the Baltic Sea and at the mouth of the River Tyne.
1:100 scale, model maker: Günther Seherr

Depth charge rack with WB-1 depth charges

Soviet Navy, USSR, 1965 'Shenzhen'-class fast torpedo boats (Project 206) were equipped with depth charge equipment shown here.

Sonobuoy (hydroacoustic radio buoy) for the detection of submarines

Soviet Navy, USSR
PLAB-type Soviet radio buoys, which could be deployed from the air, were used on anti-submarine helicopters, planes and ships. The buoys passively received the sonar signals of submerged submarines and sent the bearing (direction) by radio to their respective anti-submarine bases. In order to determine the position of a located submarine, typically three sonobuoys were dropped into the search region. In order to detect the penetration of submarines into predetermined ocean areas, bays or roadsteads, such locating buoys were often laid to form larger barriers. Sonobuoys with advanced designs continue to be used by anti-submarine divisions of naval air forces.

9 SMALL COMBATANTS

In this area you will find models of international small combatants, for example midget submarines and wreckage from a German 'Seehund'-type submarine.

10 AUXILIARY CRUISERS AND AUXILIARY SHIPS

Military use of converted merchant ships

Auxiliary cruisers were merchant vessels, converted, armed, and camouflaged with low material and personnel expenditure to threaten enemy shipping lines. They were deployed on either side, British and German, during both world wars. Particularly during the Second World War, the success of the German auxiliary cruisers forced the Royal Navy to develop elaborate counter-measures. Nine of these auxiliary cruisers were twice as successful against international merchant shipping as the rest of the German surface warships put together and tied down enemy naval units and aircraft. They stayed at sea for up to two years on their voyages. Their commanders gener-

'U 53' hunting down the Norwegian sailing ship 'Asheim' off the Scottish coast by Claus Bergen in 1917, watercolour

Display case
Felix Graf Luckner

ally treated shipwrecked persons of foreign states humanely. Deployment of auxiliary cruisers eventually was paralysed by the end of 1942 due to a lack of replacements for lost vessels.

Apart from being deployed as auxiliary cruisers, merchant ships were used in both world wars as auxiliary minesweepers, supply ships, escort vessels for small units or night-fighter-direction-vessels supporting for example the Luftwaffe defending the Reich against Allied bombing raids.

Small travel chest and autograph picture of Count Luckner
Germany
Felix Graf Luckner was a dazzling and multifaceted personality. Depending on the country he was in and his specific audience, in his lectures he presented new variations of his adventures and his acquaintances with famous people. In so doing he often mixed fact with fiction. Tearing phone books apart during public appearances won him a legendary status.

'Pirate flag' of the auxiliary cruiser 'Seeadler'
Imperial Navy, Germany
This flag comes from the estate of Felix Graf Luckner. The 'Pirate of the Kaiser', during his seven-month deployment on the 'Seeadler', captured a total of 15 ships.
1:100 scale; model maker: Christian Stührmann

'Seeadler', formerly 'Pass of Balmaha'
Auxiliary cruiser, Imperial German Navy
The American full-rigged ship 'Pass of Balmaha' was captured as a prize by a German submarine in 1916. In the course of conversion to an auxiliary cruiser, it received an auxiliary engine, hidden cargo and crew rooms, quarters for up to 400 prisoners and heavy armament. As a sailing ship, the 'Seeadler' had the advantage that constant supply with coal wasn't necessary. Early in August 1917, the ship foundered on the island of Mopelia (Maupihaa/Society Islands) due to carelessness.
1:100 scale, model maker: Christian Stührmann

Felix Graf Luckner: 'Der Seeteufel' ('The Sea Devil')
In May 1920, this non-fiction novel was translated into many languages. The US edition alone, published under the name of the bestselling author Lowell Thomas, sold over a million copies. Parts of the popular book were written by ghostwriters and are purely fictitious.

'Atlantis' ('Ship 16'), formerly 'Goldenfels'
Auxiliary cruiser, German Kriegsmarine
The freighter 'Goldenfels' of the German steamship company 'Hansa' in Bremen was converted into an auxiliary cruiser in only 99 days at the beginning of the war. After a journey of 622 days, during which 'Ship 16' captured 22 merchant ships under Kapitän zur See Bernhard Rogge, the 'Atlantis' was intercepted and sunk in the South Atlantic on 22 November 1941 by the British cruiser HMS 'Devonshire'.
1:100 scale

Small travel chest and autograph picture of Count Luckner

David against Goliath

There were numerous studies, designs and experiments for developing submarines, until the first fully functioning submarine was built by Wilhelm Bauer in 1856. Particularly, the countries that were inferior at sea regarded the submarine as an instrument for gaining a military advantage. From 1906, submarines were part of all large navies, often, however, regarded with scepticism by the older, higher-ranking officers. The First World War dispelled any doubts as to the submarine's potential for offensive operations after the German "U 9" sank three British armoured cruisers within 75 minutes in the North Sea on September 22, 1914. In both Wars, Germany became the pioneer of submarine warfare. Great Britain responded by introducing the convoy system and improving technologies for detecting and combating submarines and deciphering radio messages. There were leaps in the technological development of submarines in both world wars. Within four decades, submarines matured from relatively primitive vessels to ultra-sensitive, soundlessly operating, lethal weapons of war. The development continued during the Cold War – towards the submarine with nuclear and fuel cell propulsion, armed with state-of-the-art torpedoes and intercontinental missiles, and possessing the capability of operating even at great depths and in shallow coastal waters.

'H.L. Hunley'

Confederate States of America
On 17 February 1864, the Confederate 'H.L. Hunley' sank the screw sloop-of-war USS 'Housatonic' with a spar torpedo. This was the first wartime loss of a ship to a submersible. Shortly after its success, however, the 'H.L. Hunley' itself sank for unexplained reasons.
Scale 1:20, model construction: Maurice Verhaaren

'U 9', U-Boat, Imperial German Navy
On September 22nd 1914, 'U 9' under the command of Otto Weddigen, sank three British armoured cruisers. Not only the Admiralty was surprised by the destructive potential of a single submarine. The U-Boat thus established itself as an offensive weapon and important factor in naval warfare.
Scale 1:100

'H.L. Hunley'

Commander Otto Weddigen and 'U 9'

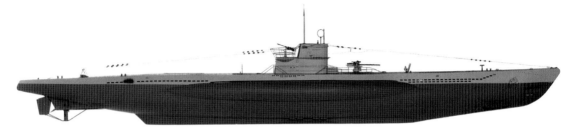

'U 96'

'U 96'
U-Boat, German Kriegsmarine
The novel 'Das Boot' by Lothar-Günther Buchheim is based on the experiences and journal entries of the author during one mission of 'U 96'. The commanding officer of this type VII C-boat was Lieutenant-Commander Heinrich Lehmann-Willenbrock.
Scale: 1:33

Extra leather clothing from 'U 96'
Special leather uniform ('Lederpäckchen') of Heinrich Lehmann-Willenbrock.

S.M.S. 'Vulkan', salvage ship for submarines, Imperial German Navy
On January 17th, 'U 3' sank due to a diving accident in Kiel harbour. She was the first U-boat lost by the Imperial Navy. The boat was raised by the 'Vulkan' and was repaired. 1:100 scale,
model maker: Günther Seherr

2 cm Flak 38 in M 44 twin mount
German Kriegsmarine, 1944
The 2 cm anti-aircraft cannon was the main light anti-aircraft weapon on all German warships during the Second World War. It was mounted as either a single, twin or quadruple set of guns. The practical rate of fire per barrel was 240 rounds per minute, and the maximum firing range was 4,800 metres.

'Agosta' (1977)
Submarine, France
'Agosta' class submarines were the last French submarines to be outfitted with diesel-electric propulsion and conventional weapons. Since 2001, France has only commissioned nuclear powered submarines. 'Agosta'-class boats reached maximum diving depths of 500 Metres and their cruising range was about 10.000 nautical miles; their speed was up to 20 knots submerged. This was a first rate performance concerning diesel-electric powered subs.
Examples of a modernized type of 'Agosta' are still in service with the navies of Pakistan and Spain.
1:35 scale, model maker: Maurice Verhaaren

Class 212 A
Submarine, German Navy
The Type 212 submarines are the world's first fuel cell propelled warships. They are powered by hydrogen and operate noise-free and exhaust-free. They convert hydrogen directly into electrical energy and are characterized by high efficiency and low maintenance requirements. Besides direct current electricity, the only reaction product of energy conversion is distilled water. The Type 212 submarine is largely independent of external air supply and, therefore, its theoretical underwater endurance is several weeks. In April 2006 'U 32' spent two weeks continuously submerged and thus set a new record for non-nuclear submarines.

Highlight:
'Leather uniform' from 'U 96'
Commander's extra leather clothing from 'U 96' in 1941 – 40 years later known around the world as Lothar-Günther Buchheim's 'Das Boot'.

TIMELINE SUBMARINE DEVELOPMENT

1776 David Bushnell developed and built the first submersible for military use. It operated by attaching explosive charges to ships. The first attempt during the American War of Independence failed.

1800 Robert Fulton successfully tested his submersible 'Nautilus'. During a diving test in 1801, it sunk a sailing ship using a dragged naval mine.

1851 The first documented diving attempt of the 'Brandtaucher' by Wilhelm Bauer. The attempt failed, Bauer and his two companions managed to leave the sunken boat via an air bubble.

1863 'Le Plongeur' was the first submersible powered by machine (compressed air motor). It employed a spar torpedo.

1864 The manually operated submersible 'H. L. Hunley' of the Confederate Navy sank the screw sloop-of-war 'Housatonic' of the United States Navy during the American Civil War by employing a spar torpedo. It was the first successful attack by a submersible: the 'Hunley', however, was also lost.

1879 Reverend George William Garrett developed and built the first mechanically powered boat (with steam enigne), the 'Resurgam (II)'.

1888 The 'Gymnote' was the first modern submarine: Powered by an electric motor, armed with locomotive torpedoes, first submarine periscope, first gyro compass on a submersible.

1900 1900 'SS 1' ('Holland VI'), the first submarine of the US Navy, and 'Narval' of the French Navy were for the first time powered by composite engines: an internal combustion engine for surface running and an electric motor for underwater propulsion.

1906 'U 1', the first German submarine was commissioned.

1914 'U-9', a diesel-electric powered submarine, sunk three British armoured cruisers with torpedoes.

1916 First crossing of the cargo submarine 'U-Deutschland' from Bremen to Baltimore. At the same time, 'U 53' was operating off the East Coast of the US.

1917 February: Declaration of 'unrestricted submarine warfare' by the German Empire: i.e. sinking without warning all merchant ships in a predefined restricted area.

1919 Germany was forbidden to construct or acquire submarines by the Versailles Treaty.

1934 The French submarine 'Surcouf' carries a seaplane in a pressure-resistant hangar.

1939 Sinking of the battleship 'Royal Oak' by 'U-47' in Scapa Flow.

1941 Capture of 'U 110' by the Royal Navy; an Enigma decoding machine and secret documents was seized; the German encoded wireless traffic was cracked.

1941 Beginning of submarine warfare in the Pacific. Japanese boats threaten primarily Allied warships, Allied submarines operate against the Japanese supply shipping; December: Commissioning of USS 'Gato' (SS-212), first of the American 'fleet boat'-classes.

1943 During 'Black May' 41 U-Boats were lost as a result of Allied counter-measures ('Ultra'); the German submarine offensive in the Atlantic was stopped.

1943 Introduction of snorkel masts on German U-Boats in order to operate diesel-engines while partly submerged.

1944/45 Commissioning of U-Boat-types XXI and XXIII; due to their large battery capacity for extended undersea cruising range and high speed while submerged, they were the first 'submarines'.

1944 Construction of the Type XVII Walther experimental submarines, hydrogen peroxide propellant and optimised hull form for a high underwater speed of 25 knots.

1945 Sinking of the 'Wilhelm Gustloff' refugee ship by the Soviet submarine 'S 13', with approximately 9,000 deaths, the greatest maritime tragedy caused by a submarine.

1947 USS 'Cusk' (SS-348), the first submarine to fire a 'Loon' type guided missile, based on the German V-1. The jet bomb could only be launched while the sub was on the surface.

1954 USS 'Nautilus' (SSN 571) was the first submarine with nuclear propulsion; its armament remained conventional (torpedo tubes).

1959 The first nuclear powered submarine with ballistic missiles was commissioned: USS 'George Washington' (SSBN-598); the 'Polaris' type missiles could be launched while submerged.

1961 The first Soviet submarines with nuclear propulsion and ballistic missiles (NATO code 'Hotel' class) enter into service; the boats had to surface for rocket launch.

1963 USS 'Thresher' (SSN-593) implodes during a deep dive test at about 400 meters. She was the first nuclear powered submarine lost due to an accident.

1972 Commissioning of the largest diesel-electric submarines: Soviet 'Tango' class with more than 3,000 tons displacement [museum boat in Hamburg]

1976 Commissioning of the first submarine of the 'Los Angeles'-class. With 62 units built, these attack submarines belong to the most numerous nuclear powered class of subs ever commissioned.

1981 World premiere of the film 'Das Boot'.

1981 Commissioning of the Soviet nuclear-powered submarines with ballistic missiles of the Project 941/'Akula' (NATO-Code 'Typhoon'-class). With 48,000 tons displacement while submerged they are the largest subs ever built.

2000 Russian submarine 'Kursk' K 141, Project 949 A, NATO-Code 'Oscar II'-class) explodes and sinks during a fleet manoeuver. Official statement: A torpedo misfire.

2004 The 'U-31', the first submarine powered by fuel cells, is put into service.

2007 Since the end of the Cold War 100 nuclear powered submarines were scrapped in the US.

2010 In Russia 130 nuclear submarines are to be scrapped; the disposal of the nuclear reactors and nuclear fuel rods requires international assistance.

2013 China commissioned the fourth submarine with ballistic missiles of the 'Jin'-class.

2027 The first boat of the 14 'Ohio' class nuclear submarines employed since 1984 will be decommissioned.

Reduced to structural symbolism, Asmus

12 THE BATTLE OF JUTLAND

Naval forces in the First World War 1914–18

The First World War was the first total economic war. For the first time in history, a war was waged not only on the battlefield; it was also specifically directed against the industry and the civilian population of the enemy state. The long-distance blockade of the German coast by the Allied powers Britain and France prompted the Central Powers (the German Empire and Austria-Hungary) first to launch a war on commerce according to prize law and then engage in unrestricted submarine warfare, which led to sharp protests from the neutral states, particularly the USA. The long-expected decisive battle of the expensive "Dreadnoughts" never came about. The German and British battle fleets clashed at the Battle of Jutland, but the German Empire failed to achieve a strategic victory. It was the war of submarines and torpedo boats, of minelayers and naval aircraft which dominated the scene from now onward. And this war was no less appalling and no less brutal than the engagements between big battle fleets.

'The Battle of Jutland'

'The Battlecruiser action'
'The first battle about turn'
'Crossing the T'

Asmus Petersen (born 1928) Acrylic on canvas, 1981
Reduced to structural symbolism, Asmus Petersen represents the fleet movements during the Battle of Jutland. His artistic interpretation of events is based on careful research of historical facts. The drawings read like short logs of combat actions, even though they are no sketches of actual combat scenes.

The Battle of Jutland display case

The battle of Jutland, 31 May 1916, is considered to be one of the largest and deadliest naval battles in history. There was no winner, but 8,645 victims on this gloomy day in the North Sea. Victims such as the 589 crew members of the small cruiser SMS 'Wiesbaden' (model scale 1:100, model maker: Helmut Schmid) of the Imperial Navy, which took a serious hit in the engine room and drifted immobilized between the battle lines. Exposed to heavy gunfire from the British battle fleet, the ship sank the next day – only one member of the crew survived. Among the dead was the poet Johann Kinau, known as Gorch Fock (1880–1916). He came from a family of deep-sea fishermen from Finkenwerder. His longing for seafaring – which resonates in his most famous novel 'Seefahrt ist Not' – caused him to transfer from the army to the navy in March 1916. The most famous victim of this battle on the British side was Boy Seaman First

**Battle cruiser
'Derfflinger'
during the
Battle
of Jutland**
Albert Brenet
(1903–2005)
Tempera

Class Jack Cornwell (1900–1916) aboard the cruiser HMS 'Chester': During the Battle of Jutland, despite heavy shelling and multiple wounds, he remained at his 13.7 cm gun post. He was the only survivor of his gun crew, but died of serious wounds two days later. Posthumously, Jack Cornwell was awarded the Victoria Cross, the highest British decoration for bravery in combat.

13 THE PERIOD OF THE WORLD WARS

Arms control? Maritime powers in the interwar period 1919–39

The scuttling of the High Seas Fleet by the Germans themselves in Scapa Flow marked the end of the Kaiser's dream of German sea power and colonies. The Treaty of Versailles prohibited Germany from building capital ships and submarines, and engaging in military aviation. In the subsequent years, the other powers held disarmament conferences for the first time, to decide on a limitation of naval armaments, though without success. Basically, they clung to outmoded strategies involving battle fleets and decisive battles, although World War I had clearly demonstrated the significance of torpedo boats and submarines. On the other hand, at this time, the USA, Britain and Japan in particular forged ahead with the construction of aircraft carriers. When

the National Socialists assumed power in Germany, the restrictions on the building of new ships – in consideration of the sea power Great British – were initially cautiously sidestepped, respectively regulated in the Anglo-German Naval Agreement for fleet limitation in 1935. Hitler wanted to have battleships as a counterweight to the naval strength of the great powers. His assumption that Britain would tolerate Germany's rearmament and foreign policy for long without opposition, proved completely illusory following the German invasion of Poland at the latest, which prompted the Allies to declare war on Germany.

Decisions at sea. Navies in the Second World War 1939–45.

On 1 September 1939, the shots fired by the battleship "Schleswig-Holstein" at Polish fortifications on the Westerplatte started the Second World War. After the failure of the "Bismarck" operation in May 1941, the main burden of the war, as in World War I, fell on submarines, fast patrol boats, minesweepers, and the auxiliary ships and special-purpose vessels of the navy. However, they could not match the clear material and personnel superiority of the Western Allies, which had also totally outmatched the German navy in electronic warfare and the scientific evaluation of operative data. After the Japanese attack on the US Pacific naval base at Pearl Harbor, the European

Highlight:
Model of the
battleship
'Bismarck'
– as a result of
her unusual fate,
she remains a
legend to this
date.

conflict escalated into a world war. The destruction of the US battle fleet wreaked by a Japanese aircraft carrier group set the scene for the Pacific War, which became a conflict between aircraft carriers. Battleships increasingly lost their predominant role in naval strategy. The economic potential of the US, superior radar detection, and losses that Japanese forces could not replace as easily as their enemies, compelled Japan to resort to desperate tactics such as the deployment of "kamikaze" pilots at the end of the war.With the Japanese attack on the US Pacific military base in Pearl Harbour, the European conflict developed into a world war. The extent of the destruction of the battle fleet by the Japanese aircraft carrier association, set the course for the remainder of the Pacific war. It was a battle of aircraft carriers. Ships quickly lost their importance. The economic potential of the

United States, better radio measurement tracking and their ability to replace losses faster, eventually led to desperate military measures by the Japanese, such as the start of the use of 'kamikaze' pilots in October 1944.

'Bismarck'

Battleship, German Kiregsmarine
At her commissioning in 1940, the 250-metre 'Bismarck' was the largest and strongest battleship in the world. Her task was to take part in the Atlantic convoy battles and to pin down enemy forces. During the Battle of the Denmark Strait on 24 May 1941, she sank the British battlecruiser 'Hood' and damaged the 'Prince of Wales'. The 'Bismarck' took a torpedo hit shortly afterwards by aircraft from the carrier 'Ark Royal', which disabled her; a subsequent battle with a British fleet finished her off. Nearly 2,000 crew members

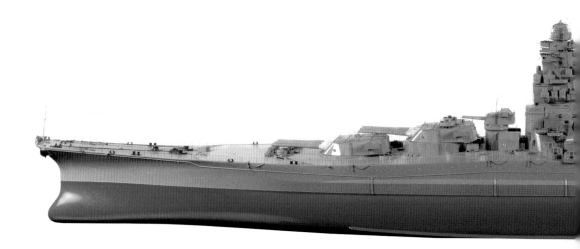

lost their lives. The 'Bismarck' had not even been in service for one year. Scale 1:100, model maker: Helmut Schmid

"'Bismarck launched'", 'Hamburger Fremdenblatt', 14.02.1939 and 15.02.1939
The launch of the 'Bismarck' took place amidst great festivities at Blohm & Voss shipyard, Hamburg. Adolf Hitler gave the ceremonial speech, Dorothea von Loewenfeld, grand-daughter of Otto von Bismarck, carried out the christening of the ship.

'The sinking of the "Bismarck" May 27th, 1941'
Charles E. Turner (1883–1965)
Oil on canvas, mounted on cardboard

'Yamato'
The battleship 'Yamato' of the Imperial Japanese Navy and her sister ship

'Musashi' were the largest battleships ever built.

With a calibre of 46 cm, the 'Yamato' had the heaviest gun armament ever carried by a warship. The armour plates of these giants reached a thickness up to 560 mm; 1,174 watertight bulkheads protected the hull against underwater explosions, they were arranged almost honeycombed. The 'Yamato' took part in the battles of Midway, Solomon Islands and Leyte Gulf (Philippines). However, considering her military potential against aerial attack without own air cover, she had no chance.
On April 7th, 1945, the 'Yamato' was attacked by bombers and torpedo planes of the U.S. Task Force 58, southwest of the Kyushu
Islands and sank. Only 269 out of 2,767 men survived this tragedy.
Scale 1:100

Highlight:
The Japanese battleship 'Yamato', she had the heaviest gun armament ever carried by a warship

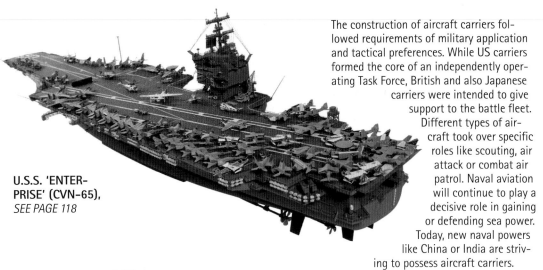

**U.S.S. 'ENTER-
PRISE' (CVN-65),**
SEE PAGE 118

The construction of aircraft carriers followed requirements of military application
and tactical preferences. While US carriers
formed the core of an independently operating Task Force, British and also Japanese
carriers were intended to give
support to the battle fleet.
Different types of air-
craft took over specific
roles like scouting, air
attack or combat air
patrol. Naval aviation
will continue to play a
decisive role in gaining
or defending sea power.
Today, new naval powers
like China or India are striv-
ing to possess aircraft carriers.

14 COLD WAR NAVIES

In this section you will find shipmodels
from the era of the 'Cold War'.

15 NAVAL AVIATION

Naval aviation – Naval warfare in a new dimension

When flying machines proved their military
value towards the end of the First World
War, they became attractive for all navies,
in the early stages in particular in the
armed scouting role. Certainly, they had to
have reliable engines and had to be capable of carrying radio equipment for long
range transmission in order to give current
situation reports at all times. Small seaplanes or land based aircraft weren't able
to carry heavy radio equipment for reasons
of structural stability. Rigid airships (Zeppe-
lins) offered an alternative, but they were
very expensive and depended on favorable
weather conditions to be of any use. In
order to increase the range of operation
of seaplanes, trials with seaplane tenders
already pointed in the right direction. But
tentative attempts to operate land based
aircraft from flying off platforms mounted
on ships or primitive aircraft carriers were a
next generation technology.
The capability of using weapons of effective
striking power against targets on shore or
against ships was gained between the two
World Wars as a result of the improvement
of the naval aircraft itself. During the Second World War this ability rose to full effec-
tiveness. Meanwhile the mighty naval powers like the US, Britain, and Japan, which
operated in the vast areas of the Atlantic
or the Pacific Ocean, had developed the
aircraft carrier into a major fighting ship.

The war in the Pacific from 1941 to 1945
was the war of the aircraft carrier. No other
weapons system in this theatre of operations
gained such an importance. At the beginning
of the conflict, both Japan and the US had
task forces consisting of aircraft carriers.
But the US Navy came out of this war as
the only seapower which, within only a few
years, developed the individually operating
"fast carrier task force" to perfection. Only
the US were capable of commissioning large
numbers of carriers, equip them with technically outstanding aircraft, train thousands
of pilots and, at the same time, create the
necessary logistic support for the military
operations of a carrier task force over thousands of miles. Their Japanese opponent was
literally crushed by this superiority.
Naval aviators are exposed to special challenges on board an aircraft carrier. Flying
couldn't be more hazardous than under
these conditions. The start, especially by
catapult, comes close to shooting an arrow
by a crossbow; flying in the disorientating
vastness of the ocean is only possible by
very precise navigation; the military mission
holds unpredictable risks; then the own
ship has to be relocated – provided it is still
there – and, last but not least, you have to
land with the aid of an arresting hook on
a tiny little deck in motion – a procedure
which resembles a controlled crash. The
work of the maintenance crew on a carrier
deck is actually one of the most dangerous
jobs, too. The simultaneous handling of
fuel, bombs or rockets amidst the noise of
starting or landing aircraft, and respectively
in the hanger deck, can only function successfully because of decades of systematic
operating experience. Not every navy is
able to maintain aircraft carriers. It is a very

complex and expensive weapons system but it is also the symbol of sea power.

USS 'Intrepid' (CV 11), aircraft carrier, US Navy

The 'Intrepid' was one of 24 fleet carriers of the 'Essex'-class. During the Second World War she took part in the landing operations on Saidor (New Guinea) in January/February 1944 and in the Battle of Leyte Gulf in October 1944. She was heavily damaged several times by Japanese torpedoes and 'kamikaze' aircraft. Scale: 1:160. Model maker: Miroslav Tesar

Grumman TBF(M)-3 Avenger, 1945 torpedo bomber, USA

The 'Avenger' was developed in 1939–1941 by the Grumman company. The first flight of the TBF-1 model took place on August 7, 1941. Since 1943, the torpedo bomber was one of the U.S. Navy's standard carrier airplanes in the war against Japan. As Grumman could not meet the large demand of the Navy alone, the 'Avenger' was built under license by General Motors and received the designation TBM. Nearly 10,000 'Avenger' were built. The TBM-3 model on display belonged to squadron VT-10 of USS 'Intrepid' (CV-11) in 1945.
Scale 1:32, model maker: Olaf Krabbenhöft

Chance Vought F4U-1D Corsair Fighter and fighter bomber, USA

Along with the Grumman F6F 'Hellcat', the Chance Vought F4U 'Corsair' was the US Navy's best carrier-based fighter aircraft. The Corsair was easy to distinguish from other fighter aircraft, because of its bent wings. This was due its huge propeller of approximately four meters in diameter, which had to transfer the power of a 2,000 HP radial engine. The bend in the wing extended the landing gear of this mid wing aircraft. The most-produced variant of the Corsair was the F4U-1D. In April 1944 the F4U was accepted for shipboard opera-

tions. The aircraft shown here belonged to squadron VF-84 of USS 'Bunker Hill', a carrier of the 'Intrepid'-type. In February 1945 "White 167" was flown by Lieutenant Commander Roger Hedrick, a former squadron member of the famous 'Jolly Rogers' (VF-17).
Scale 1:32

'Task Force 58', 1945, Diorama
The biggest fleet in history
The 'Fast Carrier Task Force 58' was the most important fleet of the U.S. Navy in the War in the Pacific, and arguably the most powerful in naval history. 16 aircraft carriers and their naval aviators formed the core. All other vessels, from battleships to tankers, offered protection and support for the carriers. Everything was concentrated to ensure the planes' readiness for action. This diorama shows a section of Task Force 58 at its main anchorage at Ulithi (Caroline Islands/West Pacific). The phalanx of the carrier, known as 'murderer's row', is impressive (see page 117).

'Bussard', catapult ship
1941, German Luftwaffe
With the Treaty of Versailles, German naval aviation was banned, however there was a secret realignment in the 1920s. With the establishment of a German Luftwaffe as an independent part of the Wehrmacht

in 1935, naval aviation initially existed between the navy and the air force. Finally, Göring's Luftwaffe took over its functions. The catapult ship 'Bussard' was therefore not part of the navy, but of the 'Floating Formations of the Luftwaffe'. Its design was based on experience gained with Lufthansa catapult ships and it served as a floating base for flying boats and sea planes on long-range reconnaissance missions, mainly in Norway.
Scale 1:100, model maker: Helmut Schmid

'U.S.S. Enterprise' (CVN–65) (see page 116)
Nuclear-powered aircraft carrier, U.S. Navy
The 'Enterprise' was the first nuclear-powered aircraft carrier and one of the largest warships ever built. With 51 years of active service, she was also one of the longest-lasting. Planned in the mid-1950s, she was commissioned in 1961. The 'Big E' took part in all important U.S. Navy operations of the last few decades. The aircraft carrier was decommissioned in December 2012 and by 2016 will be at Newport News shipbuilding, the shipyard where it was built, to be prepared for breaking up. The model on display shows the complete aircraft complement of the ship arranged on deck. In reality this did not occur. Scale 1:350, model maker: Hans Bosma

Ejection seat type GH7C
Martin-Baker, 1973
Ejection seats are a pilot's life insurance. If it is necessary for a pilot to exit a dam-

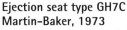

16 MODERN COMBAT SHIPS

USS 'Zumwalt' (DDG 1000), 2016
Guided missile destroyer (DDG)
'Zumwalt' class ships have a futuristic
design. This is due to their 'stealth' characteristics. Because of its inwardly sloping
vertical surfaces ('tumblehome') above the
waterline the 186-metre-long hull with its
massive bridge superstructure generates
the radar signature of a small fishing boat.
The 'Zumwalts' are powered by gas turbines
coupled with induction motors driving two
shafts. This enables an almost silent voyage.
The missiles are invisibly housed in the
body of the ship. Project 'DDG 1000' is one
of the most longstanding in the history of
the U.S. Navy. Preliminary studies began at
the end of the 1990s. Due to the enormous
costs (development costs up until 2008:
13 billion dollars; a cost of approximately
four to five billion dollars per unit) this
class of ship was reduced from an initial
32 ships to three.
Scale: 1:200, model maker: Maurice
Verhaaren

aged plane, a specific procedure is set into
place within seconds. Firstly the cabin roof
is blasted off, then the seat shoots off a
guide rod. A rocket kit then catapults the
seat and pilot several dozen metres into the
air. Then the separation of seat and pilot
follows – the pilot floats down with a para-
chute. Several hundred thousand Euros for
one seat is money well spent. Thousands of
pilots owe their lives to this equipment.
This ejection seat had been installed on a
McDonnell F4F-Phantom fighter bomber of
the German Naval Air Arm.

Highlight:
Martin Baker
Ejection seat
– a pilot's life
insurance.

DECK5

119

HIGHLIGHTS ON DECK 6

Model of the passenger ship 'Bremen' (1858).
It shows the age of transition from sailing ships to steam and propeller.

Model of the 'RMS Titanic' (1912).
The fate of no other ship has been so deeply impressed unto the collective memory.

Diorama of a historic sea rescue with line shot and breeches buoy.

Diorama of the 'Saxonia' (1982) shows a scene in the Port of Hamburg. The ship is equipped for the transport of containers, general cargo and heavy goods.

Model of the container ship 'Regina Mærsk' (1995).
As one of the first post-panamax container ships, she was no longer able to pass through the channel of the Panama Canal.

Model of the 'Cap San Diego'.
The original lies in the Port of Hamburg and is the world's largest seaworthy and operational museum cargo ship.

Model of the 'AAL Brisbane' (2010).
As a heavy-goods freighter, the original belongs among the specialised ships.

Magnificent shipyard models of the 'Buffalo' (1909) **and 'Wotan'** (1913) tankers in historical showcase. Due to their size and weight, they had to be lowered into the museum by crane.

Model of the 'Princess Victoria Luise' (1900) shows the first ship to be designed and built as a cruise ship.

Historic travel souvenirs. In 1912–13, Anna Auguste Kannengießer from Berlin travelled around the world on board the passenger steamer 'Cleveland' (1909).

Cross-section of the 'France' (1912), passenger ship, covers an entire wall. Contemporary illustrations clearly indicate the class differences on board.

Model of the owner salon of the Onassis Yacht 'Christina' shows the splendour on board a private luxury yacht. It can be completely illuminated inside.

Deluxe outer cabin of the 'Sea Cloud II' (2001) cruise ship. The original interior, on display here, was taken from this famous sailing ship.

MODERN SEAFARING: MERCHANT AND PASSENGER SHIPPING

Deck 6 is dedicated to the development of commercial and passenger ships since the mid-19th century. Sailing ships were able to maintain their position as a means of transport until the 1880s. But as reliable steam machinery and iron and steel as ship building materials became cheaper and more easily available, steam ships increasingly dominated the market. Sailing ships could not compete with the lower freight rates, scheduled transport and overall higher transport performance.

From the 1960s, standard 20-foot containers revolutionised sea freight. The TEU, 6m x 2.5m x 2.5m, has completely changed maritime trade over the past few decades. A central area of the exhibition also focuses on the passenger shipping industry. Above all, emigrants to the United States, as well as business travellers, took advantage of ships in the 19th and 20th centuries. Until the introduction of regular airline services, a sea voyage was the only link between the two continents. Today, sea voyaging is experiencing a renaissance. The Caribbean and sun decks, deck chairs and cocktails – the number of cruise passengers is steadily increasing.

During the second half of the 19th century, the era of sailing ships came to an end – steam ships of iron and steel now dominated the movement of goods at sea. Steamships were able to travel to a schedule, because they were not dependent on the wind. Ship-owners' profits increased as a result of their larger load volumes. The introduction of the diesel engine at the beginning of the 20th century made sea transport even more economical. Diesel engines required fewer crew members and saved them the laborious procedure of taking coal. The construction and operation of steam and motor vessels, was, and is, capital intensive. Traditional sailing ship owners, mostly one-man operations, could not muster the financial resources to purchase steam ships. Joint-stock companies replaced small enterprise ship-owners. From this time onwards, it was shareholders who funded a ship collectively. The high-risk business of maritime shipping mitigated the establishment of new insurance and classification societies such as Lloyds of London or Germanischer Lloyd.

In merchant shipping, charges were incurred for shipping operators. Channel, port or pilotage fees had to be paid. The amount of the tariff was calculated according to the volume of actual cargo space – the net tonnage. Crew quarters and engine rooms were not taken into account. In order to save on fees, ship-owners used crates as additional storage space for deck cargo. These 'open spaces' were designated as non-measurable

loading area and were excluded from tax payment. Since 1969, the volume of a ship's hull has been calculated, without exception, according to a new system of gross tonnage. In this way, cheating of the system is prevented and a clear measurement of size for the tonnage can be obtained.

Steamboat 'Bremen', 1858
Scale: 1:100,
Model maker: Claus-Hinnerk Klünder

Ship financing

For the financing of a ship, the capital of a single private investor is not usually sufficient. In addition, the entrepreneurial risk in the maritime trade has always been easier to bear if it rested on several shoulders. As early as 1600 AD, merchants in Holland were looking for partners for the financing and maintenance of long-distance trade. Thus, the first modern joint-stock company was formed, the Dutch East India Company (VOC). Commercial conditions of financing

Highlight:
Model of the passenger ship 'Bremen' (1958).
It shows the transition from sailing to steam and propeller.

have changed since then, though – today, ship financing uses the acquisition of interests in subsidiaries as closed-end funds with long maturities. However, the principle remains the same: There are always shareholders who collectively fund a ship or ships and expect a return in accordance with their deposit. Shares are one of the most well-known investments. They have a rich tradition in shipping, in particular since the advent of capital intensive steamships around the mid-19th century, when companies were looking for financial backers. The selection of ship investments or company shares of international shipping companies shown here, document this impressively. The colourful and artistic contribution certificates have a high value as collectibles.

sea rescue

International sea rescue.
Helping as a vocation

In the Age of Humanism, society began to conceive maritime Search and Rescue as a duty and a necessity. Many of the world's existing maritime rescue societies owe their establishment to charities or the initiative of doctors, members of religious organisations or private individuals. Newspaper reports of accidents with numerous fatalities and lack of assistance usually prompted the foundation of such organisations as well as corresponding donations. Most of these rescue initiatives initially had only a local focus but were later merged and placed under state supervision.

At the end of the 18th to the mid-19th century, three of the most important national sea rescue organisations emerged in the United States ('Massachusetts Humane Society', 1787, now 'U.S. Coast Guard'), the United Kingdom ('Royal National Lifeboat Institution', RNLI 1824) and Germany ('German Maritime Search and Rescue Association', DGzRS 1865). They are all active during emergencies in their coastal waters. Together, they coordinate the rescue and recovery of shipwrecked crew and passengers on the high seas. In 1948, they founded the IMO (International Maritime Organization), an important inter-governmental forum.

DGzRS collecting boats

DGzRS collecting boats are Germany's oldest and most famous donation boxes. This 'smallest class of boats' has been in

Highlight:
Model of the
'RMS Titanic'
(1912)
The fate of no
other ship has
been as deeply
impressed unto
the collective
memory.

service since 1875. This boat, reminiscent in form to a rowed lifeboat, became a symbol of the independence and the voluntary nature of maritime rescue work. The boat in the exhibition bears the number 8653 and is historically representative of its type. And it is still in service!

The drama of the 'Bulgaria', 1899

The voyage of the 'Bulgaria' is one of the most adventurous chapters of maritime history. The Hapag-operated ship was on its voyage from New York to Hamburg when her rudder broke and she was hit by a heavy storm on February 1, 1899. It took 24 days of great effort to install an emergency rudder and reach the port of Ponta Delgada in the Azores. In Plymouth and Hamburg, Captain Schmidt and his crew were greeted with great honour. The documents displayed in the exhibition come from the captain's possessions. They are a testimony to his personal career, but also to the drama of the 'Bulgaria': The events on board make clear that good seamanship is a basic prerequisite for safety at sea.

The sinking of the Titanic and its consequences

On her maiden voyage on 14 April 1912, the RMS Titanic collided with an iceberg weighing an estimated 300,000 tons, about 300 nautical miles southeast of Newfoundland. The ship was travelling too fast, despite ice warnings, and the lookout spotted the iceberg too late. The Titanic sank two hours and 40 minutes later. Because there was an insufficient number of lifeboats on board and the crew were unable to cope with the situation, 1,514 passengers died,

of over 2,200 people on board. The building of the Titanic had not been supervised by by Lloyds of London. She was therefore not classified, which would have been equivalent to an MOT approval.

RMS Titanic, GB 1912

North Atlantic, 15 April 1912, 2:20 am – the short life of a luxury liner comes to an end. No ship has ever gained such a level of popularity as the 'Titanic' for sinking after colliding with an iceberg. At the time of her commissioning, she was the largest and most luxurious ship in the world and was considered unsinkable. Her demise became a symbol of the ill-placed faith in the infallibility of technology. Scale: 1:150, model builder: Graupner GmbH et co. KG

The sinking of the Titanic has had consequences for rules on safety at sea:

In 1914, the SOLAS Agreement was adopted (Convention for the Safety of Life at Sea). It set down, amongst other things, the number of lifeboats for a ship. From this date, there were to be sufficient rescue facilities for all people on board and regular rescue drills were to be carried out. In addition, ships with more than 50 people on board had to keep a radio officer on watch at all times. An international Ice Warning Service for the North Atlantic was also established, as well as provisions relating to fire protection and fire-fighting. In addition, all bulkheads were to be waterproof and fireproof. A further consequence of the Titanic disaster was the exclusive use of red flares in emergency situations to prevent misinterpretation. The SOLAS Agreement did not take effect immediately, due to the

Highlight:
Diorama of a historic sea rescue
with line throwing gun and breeches buoy.

Schermuly line throwing gun

The launcher provided a line connection from ship to ship or from land to ship. With a small solid-fuel rocket, a thin line was fired which enabled stronger lines to be fetched for the operation of a breeches buoy. United Kingdom, 1950s

Hatecke freefall rescue boat

The Ernst Hatecke freefall lifeboat was an important innovation for emergency rescue services. It is completely closed and stowed at the rear of a ship, close to the crew's quarters. It drops at an angle into the water, without lengthy lowering. Model builder: unknown

Life raft for six persons

If the ship is lost, the crew must be evacuated. The use of a self-inflating life raft is often a dangerous step. Aboard the raft, drinking water, compressed food, medication, signal rockets and other life-saving appliances can be found. The decommissioned life raft displayed here comes from the container ship 'Marina'.
Donor: Briese shipping GmbH & Co. KG (Research Shipping Department) & Skyline Air Cargo shipping

Flag of the English Rescue Society, Royal National Lifeboat Institution (RNLI)

Flag of the German Maritime Search and Rescue Association (DGzRS)

outbreak of the First World War. However, individual countries implemented the provisions nevertheless. It was only in 1929 that a second version was negotiated, which finally came into force internationally in 1933. Further updates followed. They were often precipitated by maritime disasters.

Diorama: Historical view of a sea rescue in the 19th century

Under the watchful eyes of many onlookers, a maritime rescue party has stationed themselves on a cliff in an attempt to save the crew of a stranded brig. The standard equipment of the late 19th century is being employed: rescue boat, cable stretching from land to damaged vessel with breeches buoy and rocket apparatus. The latter was used to establish a connection between land and ship and to tighten the ropes for the breeches buoy. On loan from the DGzRS, Bremen

'Bremen' Sea rescue cruiser

23 m 'Vormann Jantzen', rescue cruiser, with its rescue launch 'Butscher', 1990
Shipyard: F. Schweers, Bardenfleth
Owner: German Maritime Search and Rescue Association (DGzRS)
On loan from the DGzRS, Bremen, scale: 1:25, Model builder: unknown

'Bremen', sea rescue vessel, with rescue launch, 1953
The first rescue vessel of the DGzRS was a conversion of the motor rescue launch 'Consul Kleyenstüber', built in 1931, conversion 1953. On loan from the DGzRS, BremenScale: 1:25, model builder: unknown

Load line mark (Plimsoll-line) and loading lines
The circular freeboard mark on the outside of a ship's hull, introduced in 1876, was based on a proposal by the English MP Samuel Plimsoll (1824–1898). It indicates a maximum loading line for a ship to ensure sufficient buoyancy and stability and to offer protection from rough seas. The abbreviations refer to one of the various classification societies (Germanischer Lloyd = GL) which determined the freeboard mark.
In addition to the Plimsoll line, the loading line referred to the minimum freeboard, i.e. minimum distance between waterline and deck line. For example, in the tropics, a ship could carry more cargo than in winter in the North Atlantic. The Plimsoll line corresponds to the Summer freeboard of ships in salt water. In addition to the different load lines, the letters

have corresponding meanings, e.g.: T = freeboard tropical sea water; S = summer load mark in sea water; W = freeboard sea water in winter; WNA = freeboard sea water in winter in the North Atlantic.

Cargo motor ship 'Kampen', 1983
The following quote comes from the Hamburg Maritime Office on 24/25 January 1984 regarding the sinking of the motor cargo ship 'Kampen': 'On 1 November 1983, around 20:00 local time, the German motor ship 'Kampen' capsized and sank, approximately 10 sm off the coast of South Iceland... The captain and 6 members of the 13-man crew drowned. The cause of the accident was increased listing to the port side, due to partial override of the coal load, which had become extremly soft. The ship had been travelling from Amsterdam with leaky hatch covers through which water had penetrated after several days of severe weather and had all but dissolved the cargo... According to an expert statement by Germanischer Lloyd on 20.01.1984, the ship exceeded the maximum permissible draught (after completed loading) by 5.8 cm, because on the journey to Iceland, it had to cross the border where the North Atlantic winter freeboard mark should have been adhered to.' Model builder: unknown

Personal documents of Seaman Peter Hadamek
Seaman Peter Hadamek survived the sinking of the Kampen.

German and international rescue companies

Freeboard mark and cargo motor ship 'Kampen'

3 FROM GENERAL CARGO TO CONTAINERS

The container is the foundation of today's world trade. Currently, more than 20 million boxes of steel are transported on over 8,000 container ships on the world's oceans each year. The load-carrying capacity of a vessel is specified in TEU. This is an acronym for 'Twenty-foot Equivalent Unit'. It identifies the dimensions of a standard container in feet.

The container trade began in 1956 in the United States. The standardised steel box reduced product handling and significantly simplified the transportation of goods. Containers protect the cargo from damage, are stable and have a low weight.

One of the first container ships – the 'Bell Vanguard' of 1966 – carried only 75 units of these new transport boxes. The loading volume of cargo vessels then increased rapidly. In 1996, the Danish container ship 'Regina Maersk' was launched. It was then the largest container ship in the world with a capacity of 6,500 TEU. At over 300 metres long and 42 meters wide. 'Regina Maersk' packed 19 rows of containers side by side. The current generation of container ships has a transport capacity of about 14,000 standard boxes.

For the transport of such a quantity, 7,500 trucks or 1,000 Airbus A 380 aircraft would be required in comparison. Currently, the largest ships carry 18,000 TEU, and there are plans for over 20,000. However an increasing cargo volume creates several problems. Some port facilities are now too small for these container ships. Also, the waterways of rivers and ports need dredging to accommodate the large draught of vessels. Container ships are mostly financed by fund management companies. Dividends are widely distributed in this way.

Other types of vessels are still used, as before, in addition to container ships. We have displayed a number of models on the half-deck. As well as traditional general cargo freighters, you will find tankers, bulk carriers for bulk material transport and reefer vessels for the transport of perishable goods.

From cog to container ship

To transport the quantity of goods of a modern container ship of 14,000 TEU,

... several Hanseatic cogs would have been kept busy for a whole year in the 15th century

... the general cargo vessel 'Cap San Diego' (built in 1962) would have to travel the same route 15 times

... 180 freight trains with 80 container wagons each would be required (Total length approximately 126 km, which corresponds to the distance Hamburg-Bremen)

... 7,500 trucks would be required (Total length approximately 105 km, which corresponds to the distance Hamburg-Kiel)

... the loading capacity of about 1,000 Airbus 'A 380' aircraft would be required

'Wonosari', cargo motor ship, 1952

The general cargo freight ship 'Wonosari' travelled in service on behalf of the Koninklijke Rotterdamsche Lloyd M.V.

Scenic representation
showing a longshoreman with traditional general cargo: tea chests, coffee sacks and textile rolls

Diorama 'Saxonia', *1982. A Hamburg harbour scene from the 1980s. Motor cargo ship 'Saxonia' at the quay, in front of shed 80/81. The ship was built at the VEB Neptun shipyard in Rostock for the combined transport of general cargo, containers, and heavy and bulk cargo. On the quay, two overhead cranes are depicted, loading and unloading at the open hatches. Alongside the ship lie the 'Bugsier 4' tug and the 'Minog' barge. Scale: 1:100, model maker: Manfred Bergmann*

Highlight:
Diorama of the 'Saxonia' (1982)
shows a scene in the port of Hamburg. The ship was designed for the transport of containers, general cargo and heavy goods.

between Europe and the former areas of Dutch influence in Indonesia. The ship was equipped for the tropicals trip and had two heavy cargo masts as well as four small refrigerated holds. Cabins for 12 passengers were located in a structure amidships. Scale: 1:100, model builder: Christian Stührmann

'Bell Vanguard', container ship, 1966
'German ship-owners have as yet not commissioned any special ships for the transport of containers', reported the German Shipowners' Association in March 1967. However, Sietas, a small shipyard in Hamburg-Neuenfelde, had delivered a ship for Jürgen Heinrich Breuer KG on April 26, 1966, which had been built for coastal trade with containers – the 'Bell Vanguard', launched as 'Hans Hinrich': Weighing 499 tons, and measuring 74.64 metres long, the ship was able to carry a load of 67 cargo boxes of standard type and travelled in charter of the Irish shipping company Bell from England to Ireland. Scale: 1:100, model builder: R. Ottmar model construction, Flensburg

'Regina Maersk' container ship, 1996
The ships of the Danish company Maersk illustrate the development of container ships and container traffic over the years. The 'Regina Mærsk' of 1996, shown here, was at 6,700 TEU the largest of her kind. Ten years later, she was travelling for the same company with almost twice the number of standard containers. With a width of 42.8 metres, the 'Regina Mærsk' was no longer able to pass through the locks of the Panama Canal, which made her one of the first

Highlight:
Model of the container ship 'Regina Maersk'
As one of the first post-Panama container ships, she was no longer able to pass through the locks of the Panama Canal

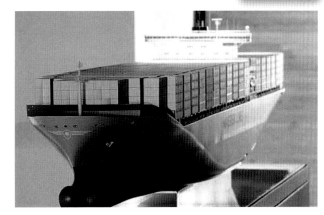

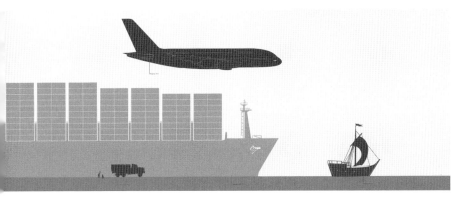

size comparison of transport

Container corridor

post-Panamax ships. Scale: 1:100, model builder: F-J Skibsmodeller, DK Munkebo

Container ship 'E.R. Manchester', 2005
'E.R. Manchester' is a modern Container ship of the lower size segment (2,824 TEU). Even the structure of her ownership represents a modern globally networked Container business. Built at Hyundai Mipo Dockyard Ltd., the ship has been commissioned by Charter Reederei E. R. Marine GmbH & Cie. After a one-month interim Charter for P&O Nedlloyd, the ship sailed as a time charter as 'Kota Pekarang' for

Pacific international lines (PIL) between the Far East, Southeast Asia and the Middle East.
Scale: 1:200, model builder: unknown

Container loading bridge
Today, loading bridges enable the rapid handling of containers in port operations. They are the visible signs of every modern container harbour. This Hamburger Hafen und Logistik AG (HHLA) bridge at the port of Hamburg, built in 1999, is located at Berth 1, Burchardkai. Its load capacity is 63 tons for spreader operation and 70 tons for hook operation, unloading stretches to 53 metres on the water side and 24 metres on the land side. The lift height is 37 metres over quay and 21.5 m under quay. The crane track is 35 meters wide. The loading bridge also has an option for automatic operation, a lashing platform and a bridge supervision cabin.

CONTAINERS IN FIGURES
20 x 8 x 8.5 feet = 1 TEU

Dimensions of a standard container
(1 TEU = twenty-foot equivalent unit):

20 x 8 x 8.5 feet = 6.06 x 2.44 x 2.59 metres

Number of containers, in circulation in 2008: 20 million

Number of containers which fall overboard each year due to accidents: 10,000

Portion of general cargo now transported by container: 70 percent

Container ships in use at the beginning of 2008: 8,000

Amount of heavy fuel consumed by a container ship with 8,750 TEU: 26,250 litres/100 km

Cargo transported per year in a container ship of 8,750 TEU: 1 million tonnes

Acquisition cost for a 20-foot standard container (TEU): 2,000 EUR

Rental for one container per day: 50–80 cents

Transport costs for a bottle of wine from Chile to Europe: 0.16 cents

Container types

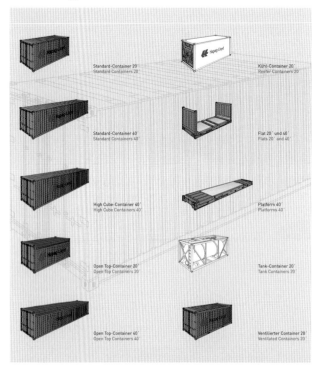

Standard-Container 20'
Standard Containers 20'

Standard-Container 40'
Standard Containers 40'

High Cube-Container 40'
High Cube Containers 40'

Open Top-Container 20'
Open Top Containers 20'

Open Top-Container 40'
Open Top Containers 40'

Kühl-Container 20'
Reefer Containers 20'

Flat 20' und 40'
Flats 20' and 40'

Platform 40'
Platforms 40'

Tank-Container 20'
Tank Containers 20'

Ventilierter Container 20'
Ventilated Containers 20'

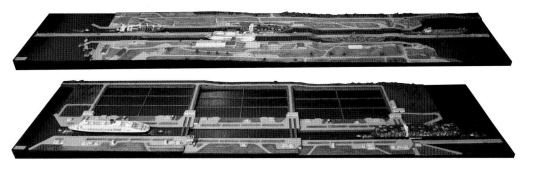

The Panama Canal

The Panama Canal, often referred to as the eighth wonder of the world, connects the Atlantic Ocean with the Pacific Ocean. At its narrowest point in Central America, the channel is 82 km long and exceeds a height of 26 metres with its locks at Lake Gatun. It shortens a voyage from the East Coast to the West coast of the United States by around 15,000 kilometres. The measurements of the present locks allow vessels with a width of 32.3 metres and a length of 294 metres to pass through. Such vessels are designated 'Panamax class'. They can load approximately 4,200 TEU. Some 14,000 ships pass through the canal each year. Larger ships will also be able to pass through after the completion of the expansion. Ships in the neo-Panamax class can be as long as 366 metres and up to 49 metres wide and load up to 13,200 TEU – almost three times as much as the old Panamax ships. The completion of the new locks is expected in January 2016.

The first attempt to build the canal was made in the 19th century by the French businessman Ferdinand de Lesseps. He had previously built the Suez Canal, but failed with Panama. In 1902, President Theodore Roosevelt bought material and construction rights from the French and concluded a treaty with Panama. In 1905, the Americans commenced construction work. Nearly 6,000 workers lost their lives due to the difficult terrain of swamps and mountains. Construction costs amounted to $386 million. In 1977, President Carter and Head of State General Omar Torrijos agreed the return of the canal to Panama by 2000. The canal has had great military importance for the United States. Battleships built up until 1914 were able to pass through the canal, as well as battleships used in the Second World War and aircraft carriers. Following the extension in 2016, the most modern and the largest aircraft carriers of the U.S. Navy will be able to pass through.

Diorama: The old and the new Gatun locks in the Panama Canal

Ships coming from the Caribbean travel through Limon Bay into the canal. After 10 km, the three-stage locks are reached, which lift vessels up to 26 meters, the level of Gatun Lake. The lake, which is approximately 38 km long, is artificially dammed and fills the locks via underground pipes. Each chamber is 305 m long and 34 m wide. The ships are moved within the locks by electric locomotives. The new Gatun locks, which should become operational in 2016, are 427 m long and 55 m wide. Here, ships will be pulled by tugs so that only ships of up to 366 m in length and a width of 49 m will be approved. A special feature of the new system of locks is the lateral retention basin, which enables better use of the water.
Model builder: Roland Klinger

4 CARGO SHIPS

Types of maritime cargo ships

Steam ships and, after the introduction of the diesel engine, cargo motor ships, transported general cargo and bulk goods either on fixed routes (where many ships also had facilities for passengers), or they carried mainly bulk goods as tramp shipping. Until the introduction of the container vessel, these vehicles formed the backbone of global trade at sea.

Container ships carry stackable, standardised boxes (containers). They have replaced cargo motor ships for general cargo since the 1960s.

Ro/ro ships ('roll on / roll off') carry mainly moving goods, with the load mostly transported on and off board by trucks.

The packet trade brokers. Mediator between ship and cargo

The Line Broker was a profession before the introduction of the container. A Line Broker represented shipowners who ran their ships according to a fixed timetable. He had the task of charging for scheduled services on offer and had to procure the necessary papers. In the showcase, objects of his everyday work are exhibited, including a bill of lading. The details of the load were also listed in a manifest. These documents are required at the port for customs clearance.

The tramp shipbroker. Mediator between ship and bulk load

Tramp brokers provide shipping space on bulk carriers and tankers. Shipped commodities include iron ore, crude oil, coal and cereals. In contrast to line shipping, where ships travel on fixed routes at fixed times, the tramp journey is on request. It is comparable to a taxi. Each voyage is unique for the Tramp broker. He has to clarify several aspects with ship-owners and charterers. The selection of a suitable vessel is at the centre of this. He also mediates between the two parties regarding pricing for freight. The outcome of the negotiations results in a freight contract (charter party).

Heavy cargo vessels are cargo ships for the transportation of heavy and bulky cargo.

Reefer vessels transport perishable goods in refrigerated holds, today also in refrigerated containers. They can reach high speeds.

Bulk carriers carry mostly bulk materials; their size equals that of tankers.

Tankers are used for the transport of liquid substances. The most well-known examples are the huge crude oil tankers or those special ships that can load petrochemical products.

Tractors are powerful vehicles. They serve larger vessels as manoeuvring aids in narrow waters or salvage wrecked ships on the high seas.

Cargo steam ship
'Caledonian Monarch', 1928
Scale: 1:96, model builder: A. H. Williams

Cargo steam ship **'Cap San Diego'** 1962.
Scale: 1:100, model builder: J. Hinrichsen, Hamburg

Cargo steam ship **'Santa Teresa'** 1953
Scale: 1:100, model builder: Christian Stührmann

SPECIAL SHIPS

Ro-ro heavy cargo vessel 'Brocken',
1976 Scale: 1:100, model builder: Manfred Zinnecker

Ro-ro cargo motor ship 'Kaptan Necdet Or', 1977
Scale: 1:100, model builder: G. Malorny

Highlight:
Model of the 'Cap San Diego'
The original lies in the port of Hamburg and is the largest seaworthy and operational museum cargo ship.

'AAL Brisbane', 2009.
Cargo ship for transporting heavy cargo, equipped with four heavy-lift cranes and an auxiliary crane. Scale 1:1000, model builder: Modelart Maciej Kowalski, Gdynia

Multi-purpose barge 'P 10', 1978
A barge is a cargo container that is not self-propelled. It is pulled or pushed by a motorised vessel and is comparable to a goods wagon. Heavy-goods barges like the 'P 10' can dive under their load like a dry dock to take or unload goods. The 'P 10' is capable of transporting drilling and production platforms, even in rough seas. The high structure remains dry even in its lowered state. Scale: 1:100, model builder: Unterweser Model Construction, Bremen

Coastal and Harbour tug 'Smit Nederland', 1979 Scale: 1:35, model builder: unknown

Bulk carrier 'Hai Wang Xing', 1995 Capacity: 39,500 t wheat. Scale: 1:150, Model builder: Georgi Modellbau, Berlin

Bulk carriers transport bulk goods.
The growth of the international economy since the 1950s required the transport of iron ore, coal and wheat to a far greater extent than previously. Industrial consortiums enabled goods to travel on fixed routes within a fixed time window on chartered vessels. Operating costs were therefore minimised. The largest ships of this type carry iron ore with a capacity of about 300,000 tons. Bulk carriers have a different silhouette to tankers. They are best identified by the hatches on the upper deck.

Tankers
After the first world war, but especially after 1945, the transport of crude oil with tankers gained importance. The oil was not refined in the producing countries, but closer to the major consumer markets in the United States, Europe and Japan. Advances in shipbuilding technology and the economic benefits of large vessels led, within a few decades, to ship units of gigantic dimensions. Crude oil tankers can reach a capacity of 500,000 tons. The so-called product tankers are another type of tanker. They carry refined products such as gasoline, kerosene, liquefied petroleum gas or paraffin. Their size depends on the port facilities and the quantity of orders by customers in the chemical industry. Because of the flammability of their load, they require very complicated transshipping devices. Transport costs per tonne are therefore much higher than for crude oil tankers.

Highlight:
Model of the 'AAL Brisbane' (2010)
As a heavy-goods freighter, the original counts as a specialised ship.

Highlight:
Magnificent shipyard models of the 'Buffalo' (1909) and 'Wotan' (1913)
tankers in historical showcase. Due to their size and weight, they had to be lowered into the museum by crane.

The 'Buffalo' tank steamer

Shipyard model of the 'Buffalo' tank steamer of the German-American Petroleum Company from 1909.
Scale: 1:50

'Wotan' motor tanker

Shipyard model of the motor tanker 'Wotan' of the German-American Petroleum Company built in 1913.
Scale: 1.50

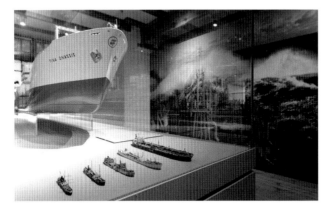

'Tina Onassis', tanker, 1953

Scale: 1:100, model builder: Christian Stührmann

'Esso Deutschland', turbine tanker, 1976

The 'Esso Deutschland' changed hands many times. Its story sounds like a tax-avoidance strategy turned steel. Built in Japan, the ship was delivered to Esso AG, Hamburg, in 1976. Seven years later, the tanker was delivered to T.T. Grand Co. of Monrovia in West African Liberia and renamed the 'Grand'. Since 1987, the ship has been under the management of the Hellespond Steamship Co. Its home port was specified in 1988 as the 'Trust territory of the Pacific Islands' – a tiny group of Islands under American administration. In 1989, it travelled under the ownership of Papachristi ship management, based in Majuro, another Pacific island group. In 1990 it was sold to Hellespond Grand Co, not to be confused with the Hellespond Steamship Co., in whose possession it once was and who again managed it in 1992. The former 'Esso Deutschland' was scrapped in Alang, India, in 2003. On permanent loan from Esso Deutschland GmbH, Hamburg; Model builder: Ihlenfeldt & Berkefeld, Hamburg

Product tanker 'Boraq', Saudi Arabia, 2003

The model is a gift from Hyundai via Walter J. Hinneberg GmbH. Scale of 1:100, model builder: unknown (probably shipyard model from Hyundai)

Oltmann Jaburg (1830–1908), Riedemann Tanker 'Deutschland'

The first tank steamer built in Germany. 'Deutschland' by ship-owner Wilhelm Anton Riedemann was launched from Vulcan Stettin shipyard in 1893. Its customer was the Deutsch-Amerikanische Petroleum Gesellschaft (DAPG) in Hamburg, to which Riedemann belonged. Oil on canvas, 1895

5 TRAVEL TO THE HORIZON

From the middle of the 19th century, first steam, and then motor vessels, replaced sailing ships. This overriding march of technology resulted in a lasting change of passenger traffic at sea. Soon, ships were running according to fixed timetables and itineraries.

Riedmann Tanker 1895

In the early days of regular steamship connections, passengers mainly used mail ships to travel overseas. However, very soon, large fast steamers started running on the trans-Atlantic routes between Europe and North America. There was a particular reason for this. Initially, it was business travellers who made use of the liners, but during the 19th century, millions of emigrants made their way to the new world by sea. It was difficult to travel on sailing ships. Confined spaces, long voyages and lack of hygiene often made travel a torture. With the advent of steam vessels, the voyage could be made a lot more pleasant. International shipping companies advertised to attract passengers. Competition between shipping companies led to ever-faster ships, and offered passengers first-class luxury and emigrants tolerable crossings.

From the 1960s onward, aircraft took over passenger transport. Emerging mass tourism, however, led to a rebirth of sea voyages. Passenger ships were henceforth largely restricted to pleasure trips. Instead of travelling as quickly as possible from A to B, the journey itself is now the goal. Our exhibition documents the history of passenger ships based on ship models, paintings, table decorations and double-berth passenger cabins. Mega yachts represent a special kind of luxury travel. A special section is dedicated to them.

Cruise ships
'Princess Victoria Louise', 1900
'With the local shipyard Blohm & Voss, I will contract the construction of a steamer that is going to be unique. A large yacht will be built, which will transport neither goods nor post, but will be set up for first-class travel.' This was how Albert Ballin, General Director of the Hamburg-American Packetfahrt-Actien Gesellschaft (HAPA) since 1899, described this 'very unique ship'. The ship referred to was the 'Princess Victoria Luise', the mother of all cruise ships. She completed her maiden voyage in 1901. The Mediterranean, the fjords of Norway AND the Caribbean were her travel routes. In December 1906, only five years after her commission, the ship stranded near Kingston, Jamaica.
Scale: 1:100 model builder: Claus-Hinnerk Klünder

Tableware passenger ship
'Queen Mary 2' The dinner service was made available by the Cunard line.

Around the world travel on the passenger ship 'Cleveland', 1912–1913
Since 1891, the Hamburg-Amerikanische Packetfahrt Actien Gesellschaft (HAPAG) has offered cruises in the modern sense. Even the first voyage around the world with a passenger ship took place under the HAPAG flag: The 'Cleveland' steamer, launched in 1908 from Blohm & Voss in Hamburg, circled the world from October

1909 to February 1910. Anna Auguste Kannengießer, a teacher from Berlin and daughter of a wealthy family, booked cabin 117 for the Cleveland's third world tour, from November 1912 to May 1913. It was a voyage from Villefranche-sur-Mer, on the French Mediterranean coast, eastwards to San Francisco. The price for the trip amounted to 6,000 marks, which would today equal about 30,000 €. Ms Kannengießer recorded her world tour in a journal, which gives us a chronicle of life on board. She also left a jewellery box of thuja wood, in which she kept mementos of her travel – a unique document of the time. The inheritance from Anna Auguste Kannengießer was made available by Ulrich Schlodtmann.

Grand piano for the Norddeutscher Lloyd fast steamship, 1906
In the era of ocean liners, a grand piano to entertain first-class passengers was an integral part of the entertainment programme. Especially on the fast steamers of the major shipping lines, they were richly embellished and adorned the lounge, although due to conditions at sea, had to be built with extra stability.

This mahogany grand piano was built by the company Julius Feuerich in 1906, for the Norddeutscher Lloyd, Bremen. The passenger ships of this company travelled the classic North Atlantic route.

Portrait of Albert Ballin
Albert Ballin (1857–1918) was one of the leading figures of maritime history. Nobody embodies the change of passenger shipping, from the transportation of emigrants to classic 'ocean liners', more than he does. Within a few years, the young, successful agent for emigrants from Hamburg became Hapag's Head of the Passage Department. Prior to 1914, it was the largest shipping company in the world. In 1899, Ballin became its General Director. He had earlier invented a new concept of travel: the cruise, referred to by him as the 'pleasure trip'.
This son of a Jewish cloth maker was influential in his new position and a confidant of Kaiser Wilhelm II. Ballin tried in

Highlight: Cross-section of the 'France' passenger ship (1912), covers an entire wall. The contemporary graphic shows class differentiation on board.

Querschnitt des SCHNELLPOSTDAMPFERS "FRANCE»

COMPAG

vain to prevent a military conflict between Germany and England. The defeat of the German Empire in the First World War ruined his life's work. On November 9, 1918, on the same day that the Emperor abdicated, Albert Ballin died in Hamburg from an overdose of drugs.

Steam ship 'Hammonia', 1855

The 'Hammonia' was the first steam ship by Hapag, which was founded in 1847. She was launched on 3 May, 1855. The 'Hammonia' was not immediately available to Hapag for passenger, mail and emigrant traffic. The Hamburg-based shipping company accepted a charter from the French Government to use the ship for troop transport in the Crimean War. On 1 July, 1856, the 'Hammonia' undertook her maiden voyage under the Hapag flag from Hamburg to New York. The crossing took about two weeks in those days. The use of the lower decks for immigrants was, at the beginning, somewhat less substantial than expected because the crossing with a steam ship was more expensive than with a sailing ship. The 'Hammonia' was in service for eight years with Hapag. In 1864, the company sold the ship to the Allan line, Liverpool. Scale of 1:100, model maker Claus-Hinnerk Klünder

Passenger ship 'Bremen', 1938 (1959)

During the 1950s, the Norddeutscher Lloyd attempted to build on its great tradition in passenger travel on the North Atlantic. New construction was, however, not financially viable for the Bremen shipping company. Therefore, the compa-

ny acquired the 'Pasteur', built in France in 1939: The ship with its prominent single chimney was completely rebuilt. Until 1971, the new, fifth 'Bremen' was in service on the classic Bremerhaven–New York route. She sank in the Indian Ocean in 1980, on her voyage to be scrapped. Scale of 1:200, model maker Claus-Hinnerk Klünder

Albert Brenet (1903–2005)

'Imperator' in New York
HAPAG's fast steamer 'Imperator' was launched on 23 May 1912, from the Vulcan Shipyard in Hamburg. The ship received its name in honour of the German Emperor, who also launched her. The fast steamer, at the time the largest ship in the world, was one of the famous trio of 'Ballin's big steamers': 'Imperator', 'Vaterland' and 'Bismarck': Tempera, o. J.

'Durban Castle' passenger ship, 1938

Alongside the legendary Cunard Line, the Union-Castle Mail Steamship Co. was one

Albert Brenet (1903–2005) 'Imperator' in New York

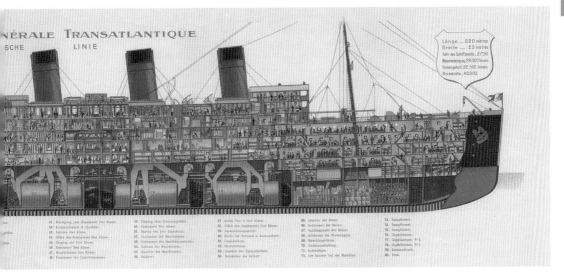

of the most popular shipping companies in the United Kingdom. The traditional trade of the shipping company, which was disbanded in 1982, was the post steamer link between South Africa and England. 'Durban Castle' was built as a passenger ship of medium standard for the around-Africa service. Scale: 1:200 Model builder: unknown

'Exodus', 1928 (1947)

The story of the 'Exodus' is the story of its passengers. European Jews who had survived the Holocaust and were wandering around devastated Europe as 'displaced persons', tried to travel overseas to Palestine after the Second World War. For this purpose, the underground organisation 'Haganah' chartered ships such as the 'President Warfield', an American pleasure boat built in 1928. The voyage of the refugee ship, now named 'Exodus', began from the French port of Sete in July 1947. With 4,514 people on board, it set off in the direction of Haifa. The British mandate government in Palestine, however, tried to prevent Jewish immigration. They feared a destabilisation of the situation. At sea, the 'Exodus' was initially monitored by warships of the Royal Navy and then encountered fierce opposition on the coast of Palestine. Three of the passengers were shot. 1,400 people were returned to Germany, where they were held in camps. The British Government only gave in after international protest. The United Kingdom abandoned its mandate over Palestine. The 1948 foundation of the State of Israel is directly linked to the voyage of the 'Exodus':
Scale: 1:125, model builder: Robert Mouat

Cruise vessel 'Mikhail Lermontov', 1972
The 'Mikhail Lermontov' reinforced the passenger ship fleet of the Baltic shipping company, Leningrad. It was built by the VEB Mathias Thesen shipyard in Wismar and modernised in 1982 by the Lloyd shipyard, Bremerhaven. It was used in trans-Atlantic traffic and in the cruise business. In 1986, the 'Mikhail Lermontov' ran aground on a reef in the Cook Strait between the main islands of New Zealand. 409 Australian passengers were rescued by the crew. A member of the engine-room staff died.
Scale: 1:100, model builder: DEWAG, Model Building Dept., Berlin

Passenger ship 'Queen Mary 2', 2004

The 'Queen Mary 2' is probably one of the most famous ships of the present day. At 345m length, 41m width and a cost of 875 million € impressively continues the great tradition of the 'Queens' of the British shipping company Cunard. With a conservative black and white hull, its interior is more in keeping with today's cruise ship standards; the 'Queen Mary 2' combines tradition and modernity. Due to its enormous size and a skilfully controlled media presence, it has a large fan base worldwide.
Scale: 1:350, Model builder: unknown

Cruise ship 'Costa Victoria', 1996

In 1996, the 'Costa Victoria' was the largest cruise ship on the European market. For Bremen's Vulkan shipyard, this also signalled the end – the ship construction company went into receivership during the development of the vessel. At 252.9 metres length, 'Costa Victoria' was able to accommodate 2,250 passengers in its 964 cabins on 14 decks. These cabins were prefabricated in modules. They had an Italian design and feel to them.
Scale of: 1:100, model builder: Georgi Modellbau, Berlin

'AIDAdiva' cruise ship, 2007

The AIDA club ship concept originated in the mid-1990s. The idea was based on attracting the younger generation with floating holiday clubs to revive the stagnant and ageing cruise market. After initial difficulties, the new concept took off. Today,

'AIDA Cruises' is one of the most successful cruise businesses in Europe. With 252 m, 'AIDAdiva' is the longest ship of the AIDA fleet to date. Scale: 1:200, Model builder: unknown.

Line-crossing Certificates. Passengers who cross the equator for the first time can take part in Equator Baptisms on board cruise ships and receive Equator Baptism certificates.

6 CABINS AND YACHTS

'Sea Cloud', cruise sailing ship
The four-mast square rigger was launched in 1931 as the luxury yacht 'Hussar' from the Friedrich Krupp Germania AG shipyard in Kiel. From 1937 she served as the largest private yacht of her time with her legendary gold taps for the American ambassador in Leningrad under the name 'Sea Cloud':

'Sea Cloud II' passenger cabin

During the Second World War, the vessel was de-rigged, armed and painted grey and deployed as a weather ship and patrol boat for the U.S. Coast Guard. The next owner was General Rafael Trujillo, dictator of the Dominican Republic. After a further change in ownership in 1969, the ship became available for charter trips under the name 'Antarna'. Today, she is employed by Sea Cloud Cruises and her home port is Valletta, Malta.
Scale of 1:100, Model builder: unknown

Passenger cabin of the 'Sea Cloud II', 2001
A cabin of 'Sea Cloud II', here a deluxe outer cabin, offers elegance, cosiness and comfort and meets modern standards. This cruise ship of Sea Cloud Cruises, Hamburg, follows the tradition of the legendary 'Sea Cloud I'. Both ships belong to the international top class of cruises.

'Hanseatic', passenger ship, 1930 (1958)
The story of the 'Beauty from Hamburg', begins in 1930 as the 'Empress of Japan'. Fairfield shipbuilding and Engineering Co., Glasgow, supplied the 26,000-ton ship in 1930 as the 'Empress of Japan', to the Canadian Pacific Railway Co., London. The 'Emmi-Jap', as it was affectionately referred to by the crew, won the 'transpacific steam record' on its voyage from Vancouver to Yokohama in 1930. After the Japanese attack on Pearl Harbor in December 1941, the 'Empress of Japan' was renamed the 'Empress of Scotland' and served as a troop transport ship. In 1958, the newly founded Hamburg-Atlantik line acquired

the ship. After its reconstruction at the Howaldtswerke Hamburg AG shipyard, the 'new' 'Hanseatic' began its service for North Atlantic tours and cruises. On 7 September 1966, the ship was severely damaged by a fire in the port of New York. The two Bugsier haulers 'Pacific' and 'Atlantic' transported the 'Hanseatic' to Hamburg, where she was soon after sold for scrapping. The model shown here is from a private collection owned by Axel Bitsch-Christensen. Scale: 1:250, model builder: Rainer Schmidt

Passenger cabin of the 'Hanseatic', 1958
The 'Beauty from Hamburg' offered only 85 places in first class. In the tourist class, there was accommodation for 1,170 passengers.

Owner Salon of the Christina yacht 1953/54
The luxury yacht 'Christina' had an illustrious owner and an unusual history. In the

early 1950s, Aristotle Onassis acquired the former Corvette H.M.C.S 'Stormont' from the Canadian Navy at a scrap value of $30,000. He rebuilt the ship into a luxury yacht in Kiel for $4 million and named it after his daughter, Christina. The Hamburg architect Cäsar Pinnau was the designer for the conversion. He also built the model of the owner's lounge. The 'Christina' was one of the first mega-yachts for private owners. Their importance was paramount in the social life of international high society in the sixties and seventies. Later, as state yacht 'Arcor', she was left to decay, but later was bought in 1998 by Greek businessman John Paul Papanicolaou. He renovated the ship once more, as the 'Christina O'. Today it is in service as a charter yacht. Model maker: Heinz Vollers

Highlight: Model of the owner salon of the Onassis yacht 'Christina', shows the luxury on board private luxury yachts. It can be completely illuminated inside.

Motor yacht 'Pelorus', 2003
The motor yacht 'Pelorus' is one of the largest modern private yachts. In the series of so-called mega-yachts, i.e. luxury vehicles of about 60 metres in length, it occupies a leading position, alongside Roman Abramowitsch's 'Eclipse' and Andrey Melnichenko's 'A'. The question of the price of such yachts is speculative but there is a rule of thumb for luxury: 'At least one million dollars per metre'. Increases are common and allowed.

After its completion in 2003, the 'Pelorus' was purchased by the Saudi politician Al Sheikh Modhassan and then sold on a year later to the Russian billionaire Roman Abramowitsch. After rebuilding at Blohm and Voss, the boat changed hands again in 2011: David Geffen, an American film and music producer, is now its owner.

Scale of 1:100, Model builder: unknown

Ferries are special ships which transport passengers and/or rail or wheeled vehicles over short routes and following a schedule. According to this definition, the train ferry over the river Forth in Scotland in the mid-19th century was probably the first ferry. Since the 1960s, international ferry services have had to respond to the rapid development of private car ownership and increasing mobility. To save time in the loading and unloading of vehicles, ferries are equipped with ro/ro ramps ('roll on/roll off') at bow and stern. These ro/ro passenger and car ferries have become a familiar sight in all ferry ports. Due to the ramps and continuous decks, they do however have safety risks associated with the danger of flooding. Severe accidents ('Herald of Free Enterprise', 1987, and 'Estonia', 1994) would seem to confirm this.

'Germany', ferry

Depending on the line and length of voyage, ferries have facilities for passengers that on the newest ships are of cruise ship standard, but resort ships are not designed for long voyages. This special type of passenger ferry, which operates according to a fixed schedule to the seaside resorts on the Baltic Sea and the North and East Friesian Islands, is furnished with a lounge. They run on short-haul routes and require only tourist demand to run.

'Germany', ferry, 1972
In 1972, the Federal Railway Division in Hamburg took over the 'Germany' combined rail and car ferry for use between Puttgarden and Rodby. The ship could be operated purely as a car ferry by installing slope decks. There was room for 12 D-train waggons on the railway deck. After 26 years in service, the ferry was sold as 'Al-Salam 97' to Felfela Inc. SA, Panama in April 1998. The ship eventually travelled for Snow Drop Co. Ltd., Kingston, under the name 'Salam', until it was sold to Alang, India, for scrapping in 1999. Scale: 1:100, model builder: Ihlenfeldt & Berkefeld, Hamburg

'Prinz hamlet II' ferry, 1969
'Prinz Hamlet II' was launched in 1969 from the Jos. L Meyer shipyard in Papenburg, as the 'Vikingfjord'. From 1970 to 1973 she operated as the ferry service from Hamburg to Harwich (GB). After being sold in 1974, she began what is a typical ship's life for a ferry. She changed owner several times and her name four times, ending up under the cutting torch as the 'Golf' in 2007.
Scale: 1:100, model builder: Unterweser Modellbau, Bremen

'Fehmarn' railway ferry, 1927
The increased volume of traffic between the island of Fehmarn and the mainland in 1927 can be attributed to the 'Fehmarn'. This steam train ferry, which was commissioned by the District of Oldenburger Eisenbahn-Gesellschaft, was the first on

'Fehmarn', railway ferry

this route to transport a passenger train. The ship railway was discontinued with the construction of the Kyle bridge (1963); railway ship traffic ceased; the ferry was sent to Italy as the 'Peloritano', where she was scrapped in 1981.
Scale: 1:50, Model maker: Christian Stührmann

'Dolphin' high-speed ferry, 1996
The 'Dolphin' ferry was built as a high-speed connection between Trelleborg (SE) and Rostock. She was delivered from the Austal Ships Henderson shipyard in Fremantle, Australia, which had vast experience in the construction of catamaran vessels. The fuselage, which was split into two halves, guaranteed a good level of seaworthiness with minimal rolling on large deck surfaces. At the water line, the ship had low rolling resistance and could reach a speed of 37.5 knots. In 2005, in Rostock, the ferry was handed over to the United Co. for Marine Lines, Jeddah as 'Almottahedah-1'.
Scale: 1:100, Model builder: unknown

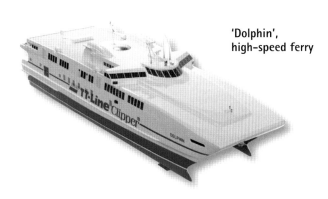

'Dolphin', high-speed ferry

HIGHLIGHTS ON DECK 7

Real samples from the seabed - Including a piece of asphalt volcano from the Gulf of Mexico.

Film from the depths of the ocean and from expeditions with spectacular insights into our seas.

Measuring equipment used at sea, such as a large sediment trap.

Fish preserved in alcohol from the rich zoological collection of the University of Hamburg show the variety of life in the ocean.

Multi-touch table allows you to follow ocean currents.

Models of the great research vessels including the three 'Meteor' ships with their history and the actual mast foot of the first 'Meteor'.

Kiel World Relief: Overscaled map of the world showing our world at all its heights and depths of our earth.

3D globe with exciting animation, including weather data and the spread of a tsunami.

OUR SEAS – OUR RESEARCHERS

Where is the deepest point of the ocean? How does a dive robot work? What are 'Black Smokers', gas hydrates and asphalt volcanoes? How is our Earth constructed, and why is the climate changing?

The major German maritime research institutes and the Consortium of German Marine Research (KDM) have worked together for the joint presentation of their work on Deck 7.

Visitors can hear what the sea sounds like and see the images broadcast by a diving robot in the deep sea. The work of Arctic Explorers in both the Arctic and the Antarctic is displayed with current and historical footage. A great 3D globe shows the development of weather patterns, the spread of a tsunami, and the seabed. The CEN (Centre for Earth System Research and Sustainability) of the University of Hamburg has provided a multi-touch table that allows visitors to explore where the great ocean currents run and how they transport energy and heat around the globe. You can also click on to particularly interesting regions for more information, graphics and short films.

Jules Verne's fantasy in model form:
Captain Nemo's famous submarine Nautilus from the novel '20,000 Miles under the Sea'.

1 THE TOUR BEGINS WITH TWO GREAT VISIONARIES OF THE 19th CENTURY:

Jules Verne and Alexander von Humboldt. Both were global citizens, both charted adventurous expeditions – one in reality, the other in his novels. The universal scholar, Alexander von Humboldt undertook what were often gruelling expeditions over several years between 1799 and 1829. These took him, amongst other places, to South America and Russia.

In his field research, von Humboldt was occupied with reciprocal relationships in nature. His work was substantial for the fields of zoology, climatology, geology and botany. He is considered to be the first scientific networker. The novels of the French writer Jules Verne provided the first contact with scientific subjects for many of his readers. Books such as '20,000 Leagues under the sea' or 'Journey to the Centre of the Earth' continue to inspire the imagination of readers to this day.

SPECIAL FEATURES
The exhibition on this deck has been developed in close cooperation with the Consortium of German Marine Research. Scientists from various oceanographic institutes take visitors on Deck 7 along with them into sea. They travel the world in international teams to enable us to better understand our planet.

KDM Chairman Prof. Dr. Ulrich Bathmann:
'It is important to open all areas of coastal, marine and polar research to the public and to create new networks and dialogues. The consortium of German Marine Research (KDM) brings the oceanographic institute to the public through a variety of activities. We have also worked closely with the International Maritime Museum for years. Deck 7 provides an impressive platform on which research highlights and the work of marine scientists can be presented in multimedia format. In addition, our KDM lounge on Deck 7 is a clear signal that everyone, from students to directors of the oceanographic institute, has a space here in Hamburg which provides the freedom to think and to discuss. Over the years, the Maritime Museum has also provided a home port for the crews of medium and large research vessels. Just as our research programmes are continuously being updated, Deck 7 is always being updated with current aspects of marine research. Recognise, be amazed, learn, understand – on Deck 7 and by our expeditions into the oceans.'

Born in 1828, Jules Verne was seen as the 'father of science fiction'. The author anticipated pioneering inventions such as the submarine, the telephone and space travel in his books.

On Deck 7, historical documents, scientific exhibits and models of major research vessels trace how the work of marine researchers has developed since the 19ᵗʰ century.

2 RESEARCH AT SEA

What holds the ocean together at its core
A visitor from outer space would view planet Earth as a water planet at first glance: 71 percent of its surface is covered by oceans. On satellite images, it shines a rich, dark blue. However, in our narrow way of viewing things, we humans have called our planet 'Earth'.

The oceans – are they just water? No – they are much, much more. 'If we take a single drop from the sea, we can see original creation being repeated', wrote the French historian Jules Michelet (1798–1874). Marine scientists need more than a drop, of course, to be able to decode the mysteries of the ocean. They take samples from all depths to determine temperature, salinity, pressure, or the composition of sea water. Using a series of monitoring programmes, they examine the large-scale circulation at all depths, are interested in the interaction between the ocean and the atmosphere, and extract sediment cores from deep down in the seabed to reconstruct the climate history of our planet. The physical conditions determine life in the oceans, as elsewhere. Sea creatures have often adapted to stable conditions over millions of years. Even small changes can seriously disrupt food chains and ecosystems. It is for this reason that physicists, biologists, chemists and geoscientists work closely together in marine research to better understand the earth as a system.

Underwater robot
Remote-controlled, unmanned underwater vehicles (ROVs) are able to take on various tasks in the exploration of the sea. The 'Marum Quest 4000' is one of the first industrial built diving robots. It was developed for research down to a depth of 4,000 metres of water and is designed to meet the requirements of the scientific community.

Highlight:
Real samples from the seabed, including a piece of asphalt volcano from the Gulf of Mexico.

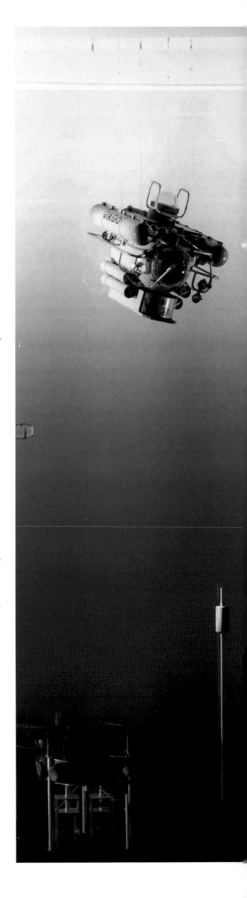

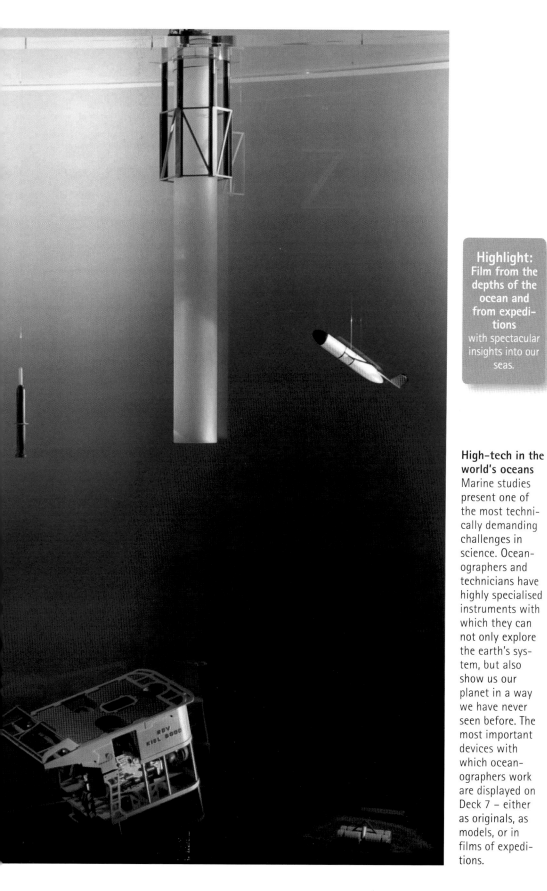

Highlight:
Film from the depths of the ocean and from expeditions with spectacular insights into our seas.

High-tech in the world's oceans
Marine studies present one of the most technically demanding challenges in science. Oceanographers and technicians have highly specialised instruments with which they can not only explore the earth's system, but also show us our planet in a way we have never seen before. The most important devices with which oceanographers work are displayed on Deck 7 – either as originals, as models, or in films of expeditions.

'Polarstern' research vessel at night near Georgia. The ship's headlights shine into the darkness.
(PHOTO: MK/vdL)

The system is very compact, weighs 45 tons and consists of a vehicle produced in the United States, a winch with a 5,000-metre power supply cable, a control container for steering, a launching frame and a workshop container. The control unit of the diving robot is reminiscent of a command centre of a space ship: The control container of the 'Marum Quest 4000' is placed on the working deck of the research vessel. Inside sit the pilots who guide the underwater vehicle through the deep sea. Its mission

is tracked on the screens. Since starting missions in 2003, the Quest has completed more than 300 dives on over 25 expeditions. In addition to the sampling of deep-sea hot springs on the mid-Atlantic Ridge, also processed were gas sources in the Black Sea, deep-sea corals from Ireland or elemental sulphur outlets near Papua New Guinea, to name but a few missions. The installation of underwater observatories and autonomous instruments on the seabed is also the task of the diving robot, as is the recovery of

Marine biologist Prof. Dr. Gerhard Bohrmann on the bridge of the 'Polarstern' during the mapping of the South Sandwich Trench.
(PHOTO: vdL)

heavy scientific equipment. The GEOMAR Helmholtz Centre for Ocean Research in Kiel hosts another German underwater robot called 'ROV Kiel 6000'.

AUVs – Autonomous through the deep sea

Torpedo-shaped AUVs 'fly' through the deep sea without any cable connection to the ship. The abbreviation stands for 'Autonomous Underwater Vehicles': These can move over longer distances and gather information from the environment with acoustic sonar. With this information they can create precise maps which show the depth profile of the oceans.

The vehicle is programmed according to its mission before starting on an operation. The system can simultaneously execute multiple tasks. To do this, different measurement systems are installed. The AUV 'Abyss' belonging to the GEOMAR Helmholtz-Centre for Ocean Research in Kiel is currently equipped with a conductivity, temperature and pressure probe (CTD), a particle sensor, a high-definition sounder, a swath bathymetry sonar, a sonar that creates depth profiles of sediment, and a photo camera. Two further scientific AUVs are available in Germany, the 'Marum-seal' and the 'Bluefin', belonging to the Alfred-Wegener-Institute for Polar and Marine Research. Worldwide, scientists are working on the further development of this class of device.

Gliders – 'glider pilots' at sea

Gliders can move under water for a longer time and for several thousand kilometres.

Bringing out a glider by Cape Verde:
A glider is launched from a dinghy into the open water, to take measurements.
(PHOTO: vdL)

They are equipped with wing stumps and powered in a similar manner to torpedoes. In fact, gliders really are 'torpedoes' with wing stumps and a compass. They have pressure-proof housing of approximately 1.5 metres in length, and can be used in water at a maximum depth of 1,500 metres, depending on the model. As well as with a battery, they are equipped with sensors and with electronics for navigation, data recording and communication. With a high-pressure pump, the glider can pump oil from an inner reservoir into an outer and back to control its depth, creating a characteristic zigzag pattern of movement. Its small wings function like a glider. If it has reached its target depth, it increases its volume again and begins the ascent. During its move through the water, it collects data on temperature, salinity and sometimes also oxygen content. On returning to the surface, it establishes contact with the control centre by an iridium satellite phone and transfers its data to the computer in the Marine Research Institute.

New view of the seabed:
Echosounder image of subjects and sediment near the Southern Sandwich Islands.
(MAP: Paul Wintersteller @ MARUM)

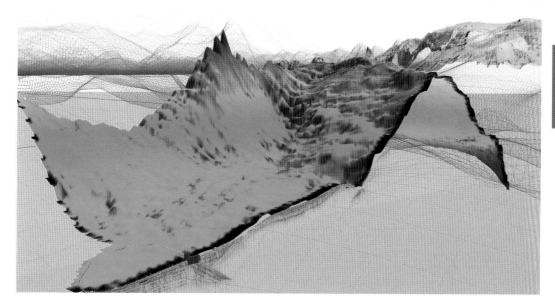

Model of the ROV
'Marum Quest 4000'

Seafloor drilling device

Sediment on the seabed offers a glimpse into our earth's climate history. The deeper the layers of the seabed, the older the deposited material. With classic devices like the gravity corer, a cutting barrel that enters the ocean floor using its own weight, relatively short cores of about 20m can be obtained. To obtain long sediment cores, oceanographers need to employ time-consuming drill boats. They are equipped with a drilling rig and can construct a drill string from the ship to the seabed of several kilometres in length. Similarly, holes can be drilled up to several hundred metres deep into the seabed. The amount of effort and cost for this procedure is extremely high. This is why, at the Bremen Marum Institute, a portable sea floor drill rig (MeBo) has been developed, which can be used by research vessels such as the 'Meteor' and the 'Sonne'. It operates by remote control in water depths of up to 2,000 metres and drills cores from soft sediment and hard rock of up to 70 metres in length.

Landers – deep sea 'space shuttles'

They land on the seabed and collect data over long periods of time. The tasks of the lander range from collecting geophysical measurements and registering seismic activity to biological experiments on the seabed. Of particular importance is the collection of material flows from the boundary layer close to the bed, such as the oxygen consumption of the sediments and its inhabitants. This is done, either by measuring chambers which are slowly lowered into the seabed, or directly with superfine micro-sensors.

Multi-water sampler – water samples from all depths

A multi-water sampler can be used to collect specific water samples at different depths. Depending on the size of the rosette, these devices can be fitted with up to 24 bottles of 10-litre capacity each. Usually a probe is placed in the middle that measures depth, temperature and salinity.

Box corer – lifting up a piece of the sea bed

Larger samples from the seabed are extracted with a box corer. This unit is lowered vertically from the ship. A weight presses the metal box into the seabed and punches out a piece that is brought on board intact. There, scientists can then examine its composition or its habitat.

Moorings – permanent measurements in the depths

For research at a specific location over longer periods of time, anchors with various instruments are used. A weight, for example an old railway wheel, anchors the mooring on the seabed. The instruments then 'hover' at a fixed depth and record their measurements. The range of embedded devices is determined by the scientific mission. Physical moorings carry sensors to characterise the water. They measure conductivity, temperature, pressure, direction and speed of current. Optical and chemical sensors are also

used, for example to measure turbidity, chlorophyll, oxygen and other gases dissolved in the sea water.

Sediment traps
Falling particles in the sea are trapped in large funnels or tubes with this device. In the laboratory, biologists, chemists and geologists study these samples to understand the size of biological activity on the surface of the oceans, where travelling substances are recycled on their way to the seabed, and the quantity of substances on the sediment.

Multinets
Alongside phytoplankton, zooplankton is the basic food of all life in the ocean. Scientists study its composition and quantity by using a multinet. The opening and closing of these five nets, or nine in larger devices, in different water depths, is controlled on board the ship. Samples may be taken at depths of up to 5,000 metres.

3 ACROSS THE SEVEN SEAS

There are oceanographers working on research ships worldwide, mostly in international teams. Each expedition requires several months of preparation. Everyday life on board is hard and very disciplined. Captain and crew work hand in hand with the scientists.
At sea, each experiment and the use of each scientific device requires a high degree of precision. Work is carried out around the clock in shifts. A research ship is not a luxury liner. Strict rules and regulations are necessary for life in a confined workspace. Curiosity and a thirst for knowledge drives the men and women on board and pushes them all too often to exceed the limits of human endurance. Together, they have one goal: to explore the interplay of physical, biological and chemical processes in the oceans.

Research ice breaker 'Polarstern' in stormy seas on its way to the Antarctic
(PHOTO: vdL)

Research ships

Research vessels from the Federal Republic of Germany are involved in international deep-sea research and cooperate with other countries in this field.

Expeditions including the research ships 'Meteor' and 'Sonne', the ice margin research vessel 'Maria S. Merian' and the ice breaker research ship 'Polarstern', are coordinated in Germany. Medium-sized research ships include 'Alkor', 'Heinke' and 'Elisabeth Mann Borgese'. Fisheries research vessels such as the 'Walther Herwig' or 'Solea' also travel in the service of science.

The research ships 'Meteor, 'Sonne', and 'Maria S. Merian' are supervised by the German Research Vessels Control Centre at the University of Hamburg. Employees at the Centre are responsible for the scientific, technical, logistic and financial

preparations of expeditions. They work closely with the expedition leaders and the contract shipping companies and regularly report to the Federal Ministry for Education and Research (BMBF) and the German Research Foundation (DFG). Together with the ship's manager, a steady modernisation of vessels is planned so that scientists will always have powerful ships available.

'Polarstern'

The 'Polarstern' is a double-walled ice breaker that can work in ambient temperatures of down to −50°C, and if necessary can spend the entire winter in the ice of the polar seas. It is one of the best-performing ships available internationally. The 'Polarstern' is able to make a speed of up to 5 knots through ice 1.5m thick. Thicker ice is broken by ramming the ice floes. Since 1982, the 'Polarstern' has spent almost 310 days a year at sea: Between November and March, she visited Antarctica and during the Northern summer, the Arctic waters. She is equipped with nine laboratory rooms, 16 winches, four cranes, two helicopters based shipside for logistical and scientific missions, as well as a multibeam echo sounder which is used to measure the seabed. Additional lab containers can be stored on and below deck.

The 'Polarstern' acts as a supply ship for the German Neumayer station III in the Antarctic.

The expeditions are coordinated by the Alfred Wegener Institute for Polar and

**'Meteor'
research ship**

Marine Research. A new POLARSTEN is currently in the planning stages.

'Polarstern' Fact Sheet
Length: 118 m
Width: 25 m
Draught: 11 m
Operational areas: Arctic and Antarctic
Travel speed: 16 kn
Crew: 44 persons
Scientific staff: 50 persons
Home port: Bremerhaven

'Meteor'
The research ship's name has a long history. So far, there have been three German research vessels named 'Meteor'. As an interdisciplinary research platform, the ship travels almost all oceans of the world and makes a wealth of research areas available to scientists: physical oceanography, maritime meteorology, marine chemistry, marine botany, zoology, marine geology and marine geophysics. Today's 'Meteor' has been in scientific service since 1986 and has travelled over 1 million nautical miles. The expeditions are coordinated by the German Research

Highlight: Models of the great research ships, including the three 'Meteor' ships with their history and the actual mast foot of the first 'Meteor'.

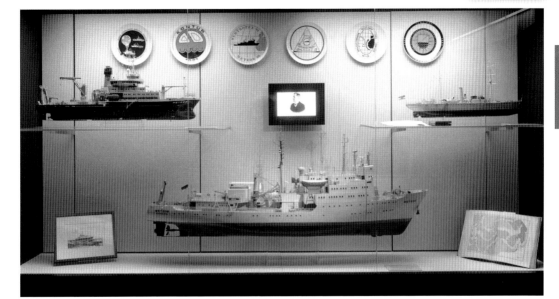

Vessels Control Centre at the University of Hamburg.

'Meteor' Fact Sheet
Length: 98 m
Width: 16.50 m
Draught: 5.61 m
Operational areas: Atlantic, East & West Pacific, Mediterranean and Baltic Sea
Travel speed: 11.5 kn
Crew: 33 persons
Scientific staff: 28 persons
Home port: Hamburg

'Maria S. Merian'
The 'Maria S. Merian' is one of the world's most powerful research platforms and is available to all disciplines of marine-based research. It was first put into service in 2006, and is therefore one of the latest members of the German research fleet. The ship is suitable for use in the Atlantic Ocean up to the ice edge, for the North and Baltic Seas, and also for trips to the equator. She can offer 14 laboratory rooms with a total of approximately 400 square metres, installation possibilities for 22 containers, and 9 research winches with

wires and cables of up to 7 km in length. The 'Maria S. Merian' is supervised by the Leibniz Institute for Baltic Sea Research, Warnemünde.

'Maria S. Merian' Fact Sheet
Length: 95 m
Width: 19.20 m
Draught: 6.5 m
Operational areas: Sub Polar North Sea (ice edge), North Atlantic, Mediterranean
Travel speed: 12.5 kn
Crew: 23 persons
Scientific staff: 23 persons

'Sonne'
Since her launch in 2014, German marine research has had a state of the art, multi-disciplinary research vessel at its disposal. With her 116 metres length and a width of almost 21 metres, the new 'Sonne' is approximately 17 m longer and almost 7 metres wider than her predecessor, which started existence as a stern trawler for sea fishing in 1969. Up to 40 scientists can be found on board the new 'Sonne', in addition to her crew of 35.

The main areas of operation for the new research vessel are the Indian and the Pacific oceans. The 'Sonne' will contribute to answering scientific and socially relevant questions relating to marine resources and the impact of human activity on nature, in particular the role highly travelled seas play in global biogeochemical cycles and climate change.

'Sonne' Fact Sheet
Length: 116 m,
Width: 20.6 m
Draught: max. 6.4 m

Operational areas:
Indian and Pacific oceans
Travel speed: max. 12 kn
Crew: 35 persons
Scientific staff: 40 persons
Home port: Wilhelmshaven

INTERNET
German Research Vessels Control Centre
www.ldfuni-hamburg.de
FS METEOR virtual:
http://www.briese.de/meteorvirtuell_2_0/
FS MARIA S. MERIAN
http://www.maria-s-merian.de
Position and route of the research ice
breakers POLARSTERN and FS HEINCKE:
http://expedition.awi.de/home

INTERNET:
KDM www.deutsche-meeresforschung.de
TIP: In cooperation with 'Marum UniSchul-
labor', the Museum Education Department
offers a series of experiments, so that
school children can learn the fundamen-
tals of science through play. At present,
the programme contains experiments on
underwater volcanics, on the flow rate of
lava and the weight of rocks, as well as an
earth plate jigsaw. Special exhibitions on
different topics, lectures and presentations
complement the range of sea exploration
topics on offer.

4 LEARNING FROM HISTORY

A glance at the history of marine exploration
shows just how young this science is. A large
illuminated display case, for example, recalls
the first German deep sea expedition. In the
port of Hamburg on 31 July 1898, crowds
saw off the 'Valdivia' to cheers of 'hip hip
hooray'. Kaiser Wilhelm II had personally promoted and campaigned for the first German
deep sea expedition. The line steamer originally run by the Hamburg-Amerikanische
Packetfahrt-Actien-Gesellschaft (HAPAG)
had thus been rebuilt into a modern research
ship – with a photographic laboratory, mi-
croscope room, laboratories, a cold room
with refrigeration unit, as well as winches
and derricks for measuring, and fishing gear.
In addition, the 'Valdivia' was equipped with
the latest generation of sounding machines.
A 0.9 mm diameter piano string wire was
used as a plumbline.
The expedition travelled from Hamburg
across the Atlantic Ocean around Africa
to the Antarctic. From there, it continued
to the Indian Ocean and then the Red Sea
and the Mediterranean Sea. On 1 May,
1899, the VALDIVIA dropped anchor again
in Hamburg. The ship had travelled over
32,000 nautical miles.
The Leipzig zoologist Carl Friedrich Chun
(1852–1914) led the expedition. In addition

Caption
First German
deep sea expe-
dition

to extensive depth soundings, biological samples were collected in particular. The haul was immense – it took until 1940 for the scientific report to be ready for publication. A popular travelogue was published in 1900 under the title 'From the Depths of the World's Oceans'. Carl Friedrich Chun writes: 'Since ancient times, the depths of the ocean have excited the imagination; this and life within it, was thought to be unfathomable, then it was thought to be

a reflection of the surface of the Earth animated with fantastic figures. Interest in thorough exploration, however, lay completely dormant until the beginning of our century. No less a figure than Sir John Ross captured a magnificent living basket star (Gorgonocephalus) from a depth of 1,500 m, which had become entangled in the plumbline, on his polar journey in Baffin Bay in 1818. In a single blow, this contradicted the idea of his French contemporary, Peron, who had proposed that the bottom of the ocean was covered with ice; this was even more convincing when it was further demonstrated that organic life from great depths was accessible even in the far North. His findings, however, fell into oblivion, and it took the silent effort of Nordic researchers to shed doubt on the Abyss Theory, put forward by the talented Edward Forbes of the British Association in 1843, which suggested that no organisms should exist at a depth below 300 fathoms (550 m).'

Konsortium Deutsche Meeresforschung

KDM MEMBERS

- Alfred-Wegener-Institute, Helmholtz Centre for Polar and Marine research
- CEN Centre for Earth System Research and Sustainability of the University of Hamburg
- Department of Maritime Systems, Interdisciplinary Faculty, University of Rostock
- German Maritime Museum

- GEOMAR Helmholtz Centre for Ocean Research Kiel
- Helmholtz Centre Geesthacht, Centre for Materials and Coastal Research
- Institute for Marine Chemistry and Biology, University of Oldenburg
- Jacobs University Bremen
- Johann Heinrich von Thünen Institut, Aquatic Resources
- Kiel Marine Science, Centre for Interdisciplinary Research at the University of Kiel

- Leibniz Institute for Baltic Sea Research Warnemünde
- Leibniz Centre for Marine Tropical Ecology
- MARUM - Centre for Marine Environmental Sciences, University of Bremen
- Max Planck Institute for Marine Microbiology
- Max Planck Institute for Meteorology
- Senckenberg Gesellschaft für Naturforschung, Senckenberg am Meer Wilhelmshaven

**Replica of the leg-
endary lifeboat**
with which the
Antarctic explorer
Sir Earnest Shack-
leton (1874–1922),
reached Georgia.
Arved Fuchs sailed
the route with the
JAMES CAIRD II and
placed the boat at
the disposal of Prof.
Peter Tamm.

Choppy sea with frigates and fishing boats, unsigned oil on wood. Jan Porcellis was born in Gent around 1580 and he died in Soeterwoude near Leiden in 1632. He probably was a student of Hendrik Cornelis Vroom (1566–1640), who was the first to choose the North Sea as a stage for his paintings and who is sometimes regarded as the 'father of all marine painting'. For a long time Porcellis stayed alternately at Antwerp and in the Netherlands; in 1622 he settled in Haarlem. Already during his lifetime he was a well-known and esteemed artist; his famous colleague Rembrandt (1606–1669) owned paintings by him.

HIGHLIGHTS ON DECK 8

MARITIME ART AND THE TREASURE CHAMBER

'Sailing boat in stormy sea'
by Ludolf Backhuysen.
The creation of plasticity using special light effects was a specialty of the artist.

'Harbour at sunset'
by Iwan K. Ajwasowskij.
In this picture the famous Russian marine painter anticipates painting principles of a later generation of artists.

"Clipper 'Lightning'"
by Montague Dawson.
These fast sailing ships were the favorite motive of this important British painter.

'The White Ship'
by Barry Mason.
A harbour painting full of melancholic romance.

'Seascape'
by Johannes Holst.
A true-to-life picture of the interaction of water, wind and clouds captured on canvas.

'Incoming fishing boats'
by Andreas Achenbach.
The 1805-born painter, was a pioneer and role model for German maritime painting.

TREASURE CHEST

Gold model of 'Santa Maria'.
The only model ship in the world, made of gold and built in authentic manner along the plank-on-frame method.

Silver centrepiece with sailing yachts – a gift from the Kaiserlicher Yacht Club to Prince Henry of Prussia and his wife on their Silver Wedding Anniversary in May 1913.

Three model ships made of natural amber – extremely rare and valuable in such fine quality.

Bone ships – a worldwide unique collection. These delicately crafted models were made by prisoners of war in England, during the French revolutionary and Napoleonic wars.

Artists have always been inspired by the vastness of the sea and its mysteries. In the 17th century, marine painting has evolved as an independent genre of landscape painting. The starting point of this artistic trend lay in the Netherlands, where economic and political development was greatly dependent on seafaring.
Representations of ships, ports and coastal landscapes bear witness to the contemporary conditions. Quite often paintings depict historical events. They also document technical developments in shipbuilding. Marine painters were chroniclers of their era. On Deck 8 the International Maritime Museum Hamburg exhibits marine paintings spanning over 400 years of art history. At the front end of this floor, in our treasure chamber, you will find ship models made of ivory, amber, silver, and gold. In this section you will also find the famous prisoner-of-war ships made of bone.

NETHERLANDS

The beginning of marine painting: Netherlands, 17th century.

During the 17th century marine painting developed into an art genre of its own. At the beginning it was solely a Dutch phenomenon. Artists painted battle scenes, famous ships, and merchant fleets, which sailed to the Far East or the New World. Ships were the symbol for wealth, national pride, and they were the means of defence.

This initial phase was followed by a development which put special emphasis on the atmospheric. Ships were no longer central, they became part of the scene. Delicate shades of grey of the northern climate, the sky and the sea in their ever changing manifestations, beaches, estuaries, and the open sea were captured on canvas.

A third phase began with the outbreak of the First Anglo-Dutch War when the depiction of battle scenes began to become popular again. New impulses also came from travel experiences which artists had collected in Italy: They brought a new kind of light – typical for the Southern climate – into the portrayal of the Dutch landscape. Other paintings were influenced by the experience of the scandinavian nature: the wild rugged landscape of the North inspired artists like Allaert van Everdingen, Pieter van der Croos, Isaac Willaerts, Jan Abrahamsz Beerstraten, Abraham Stork, Pieter de Mulier – and of course the members of the van de Velde family of artists are rated among the painters of this third period. Paintings of these artists are exhibited on Deck 8.

Allaert van Everdingen (1621–1675)
Small cargo boat and rowing boat on rough sea

Monogram on the rowing boat: 'A.v.E.' Oil on wood

Allaert van Everdingen was born on 18 June 1621 in Alkmaar in the Dutch province of North Holland. He was an apprentice to the painter and etcher Roelant Savery (1576 or 1578–1639) in Utrecht. From 1645 he was a member of the Guild of Saint Luke in Haarlem (a guild-like brotherhood named after Saint Luke, the patron saint of painters). In the years 1640 to 1644 he travelled all the way to Norway. This country's dark forest scenes, waterfalls and the surf of the Norwegian Sea

then dominated his art. His bleak images of Northern Scandinavia influenced Dutch landscape painting for a long time. Allaert van Everdingen died on 8 November 1675 in Amsterdam.

Adriaen van Diest (1655–1704)
The Action at Barfleur, May 19th 1692

sign. b. r.: 'Diest' Oil on canvas

Adriaen van Diest was born in The Hague. He was a descendant of a dynasty of painters: His father Jeronymus van Diest (II) (approx. 1630 to 1687) and his grandfather, Willem van Diest (approx. 1600 to 1678) were well-known marine painters. Like his famous colleagues Willem van de Velde the Elder (1611–1693) and Willem van de Velde the Younger (1633–1707), Adriaen van Diest emigrated to England in 1673. He probably worked in the studio of the van de Velde's in London. Adriaen van Diest died in London in 1704.

This painting depicts a naval battle at the beginning of the 'Second Hundred Years War' between England and France. This conflict was about the reinstatement of James II. to the English throne by France. James had been dethroned in 1688.

Ludolf Backhuysen (1631–1708) Sailing boat on a stormy sea

unsigned, oil on canvas

Ludolf Backhuysen was born in Emden. In 1650 he went to Amsterdam, where he worked as an apprentice before devoting himself to drawing. He became a student of Allaert van Everdingen (1621–1675). Backhuysen became one of the most popular marine painters of his time. Tsar Peter the Great took lessons in drawing with Backhuysen while he was a carpenter's apprentice under a false name at Amsterdam – providing the template for Albert Lortzig's opera 'Tsar and Carpenter': Ludolf Backhuysen painted over 600 images, many in large-format and mostly marine pictures, rarely landscapes. Backhuysen died in Amsterdam in 1708. Using special light effects, a Dutch fishing vessel is highlighted in the painting, recognisable by its typical leeboard. The creation of special plasticity by using such light effects was a hallmark of this artist.

Willem van de Velde the Younger (1633–1707)
English war ships on a stormy sea

Monogram r. on fishing boat: 'W.V.V.' Oil on canvas

Willem van de Velde the Younger was born in Leiden. He was a descendant of a famous family of artists: His father was Willem van de Velde the Elder (1611–1693) and his brother Adriaen (1636–1672) also painted. Due to financial reasons, the van

de Veldes moved to England in 1672. In London, they were in the service of King Charles II, from whom they received a joint salary. Their allocation of tasks was as follows: The Elder made drawings of naval battles and, using these as templates, prepared grisaille. The son then converted his father's drawings into paintings. Willem van de Velde the Younger is considered to be the founder of English naval painting. When the artist died in 1707 in Greenwich, London, he left behind more than 600 paintings.

FRANCE

Ange Joseph Antoine Roux (1765–1835)
The yacht 'Louisa' belonging to the Earl of Craven in the Bay of Marseille

sign. l. r. (illegible), dated 1818 Watercolor

Since the beginning of the 19th century painters could be found in all major European ports. They produced cheap yet precise depictions of ships. Their clients

Louisa, Yatch of Earl Craven ... *in the Bay of Marseilla* 1813

were mostly ships' masters or ship-owners. There was particular momentum in the city of Marseille, where the family Roux was established.

The Roux significantly influenced the formation and development of ship portraits in Europe. Their ship images in watercolour were much finer and more detailed than the majority of captains' paintings from this period and are certainly among the best that were ever painted in this genre. They also designed and built nautical instruments and issued cartographic works.

The founder of this dynasty of painters was Joseph Roux (1725–1793). Following in his footsteps came his son, Ange-Joseph Antoine, the most famous of the Roux family. Antoine's sons, Mathieu Antoine (1779–1872), François Joseph Frédéric (1805–1870) and François Geoffroi (1811–1882) continued the family tradition. Detailed ship portraits in watercolour by these artists of the third generation are also exhibited on Deck 8.

William Graf von Craven (1770–1825), the owner of the depicted yacht, was a passionate sailor at a time when sailing as a sport was still in its infancy. He was a founding member of the Royal Yacht Squadron and one of the first generous major sponsors of yacht sailing in the UK. In 1806, his ship rigged pleasure yacht 'Louisa' was launched at Shoreham docks (a small port city near Brighton on the English South coast).

Theodore Gudin (1802–1880) Rocky coast

sign. and dated l. r.: 'T. Gudin 1851' Oil on canvas

Theodore Gudin (Baron Jean Antoine Theodore Gudin), one of the most famous French painters of the 19th century, lived and worked in Paris. In his early, very detailed pictures, influences of European Romanti-

cism are reflected, while his later paintings are more impressionistic. He exhibited his works in Paris, Dresden, London and Vienna, and from 1837 was a member of the Berlin Academy of Arts.

RUSSIA

Iwan Konstantinowitsch Ajwasowskij (1817–1900)
Coastal landscape

Monogram canvas: l.l. 'A' Oil on canvas
Iwan Konstantinovitsch Aivazovsky was the son of a Feodosiya minor official,

temporary taste, but concerning colours he went beyond conventional style. If we look at the bright red evening sun and the phosphorescent green paddle boxes of the tug, he anticipates the painting principles of a later generation of artists.

UNITED KINGDOM

The beginnings of English marine painting of the 18th century.

The founder of English naval painting is the Dutchman Willem van de Velde the Younger (1633–1707). Together with his father, the painter Willem van de Velde the Elder (1611–1693), he settled in England in 1672. These two famous artists from Amsterdam responded to an invitation by King Charles II. Their studio, on the ground floor of Queen's House at Greenwich (now part of the National Maritime Museum) was the artistic centre of that epoch. The Van de Veldes' influence on marine painting lasted for over 100 years. Their paintings, as well as those of other 17th century Dutch artists, were frequently copied and their painting conventions adopted. Peter Monamy (1681–1749), one of the first English marine painters of repute, even used the name Van de Velde for self-promotion. He described his work as 'second only to Van de Velde'.

Artists such as Dominic Serres (1722–1793), Nicholas Pocock (1740–1821), and William Anderson (1757–1837), remained strongly tied to the Dutch school. One of the first to break with the stereotypes of the Dutch school was Charles Brooking (1723–1759). Misunderstood for a long time, the artist is today considered to be

born in Crimea. In 1833 he went to St. Petersburg and studied at the Academy of Arts, continuing his studies in Marseille. In 1844, Aivazovsky returned to live in St. Petersburg and became Professor of landscape painting at the Academy in 1847. Aivazovsky is regarded as Russia's most important marine painter. He left behind more than 4,000 paintings. In 1880 he donated a painting gallery to his hometown containing important works from his long career (Aivazovsky Museum). He died in 1900 in Feodosiya.

Iwan Konstantinowitsch Aivazovsky (1817–1900)
Harbour at sunset

Signed l.r. 'Aivazovsky' (Cyrillic) Oil on canvas Aivazovsky was a great admirer of the English painter William Turner (1775–1851), which is clearly reflected in this painting: In the port, its facilities are barely visible, a ship-of-the-line without rigging is visible in the background while a steam tugboat has a frigate in tow in the fore. Concerning motifs and the composition of his paintings, Aivazovsky served con-

one of the most talented – for many the most talented, and most important English marine painter of the 18th century. Paintings by Peter Monamy, Dominic Serres, Nicholas Pocock, William Anderson, and Charles Brooking are exhibited on Deck 8.

Charles Brooking (1723–1759)
A burning ship-of-the-line off a castle
signed under the rowing boat: 'C Brooking'
Oil on canvas

Like no other artist, Charles Brooking, probably born in Deptford, Greenwich, contributed to the development of a national English style in marine painting. Initially, like many of his British colleagues – he used the Dutch painters as examples and templates, but later brought a more local flavour to his paintings. He also turned away from the strict documenting tradition represented by the Van de Veldes and their successors in London. Despite his outstanding talent, Charles Brooking was denied recognition as well as financial success during his lifetime. He died in London at the age of 36, leaving behind his wife and children in poverty and need. The painting is arranged like a stage setting. It shows a night-time scenery with a burning Third Rate. The ship is moored close to a bank. Out of the gunports large flames are shooting up and the interior of the hull is lit by fire.

Dominic Serres and John Thomas Serres (ca. 1720–1793 / 1759–1825)
Liber Nauticus, and Instructor in the Art of Marine Drawing, 1805
The 'Liber Nauticus' was intended as a guide for artists and amateur painters. The book is based on an idea by Dominic Serres, one of the most important painters of the 18th century. His son, John Thomas, continued his work and published it twelve years after the death of his father. One of the rare originals is displayed on Deck 8.

Dominic Serres was born around 1720 in France. He came from a wealthy family and was destined to become a priest. To avoid this, he ran away from home and went to sea. In 1748 or 1749 he arrived in England and stayed there. Serres' talent, background and education quickly won him friends and supporters. Although he was French, he became the most successful painter of the Seven Years War and the American Revolutionary War, on England's side. George III appointed him marine painter to the King. In 1768, Dominic Serres became the founding member of the Royal Academy; until his death in 1793, he exhibited regularly at the Academy.

His eldest son and student, John Thomas Serres, was born in 1759 in London. After the death of his father, John Thomas

succeeded his father to become marine painter to the king. His successful career came to an end when his wife laid claim to the estate of the Duke of Cumberland, a brother of the King, believing she was his illegitimate daughter.

Dominic Serres (ca. 1720–1793) Morning. War ships of the red squadron in a calm

sign. and dated l. l.: 'D. Serres 1790' Oil on wood

This painting depicts English battleships on the eve of the French revolutionary wars. Five ships of the Red Squadron (the middle of the line of battle) are drifting in a calm. In the centre of the painting a First Rate ship-of-the-line is depicted. The three-decker is setting all sails. The red pennant in the foretop indicates that this is the ship of the Admiral of the Red.

Dominic Serres (ca. 1720–1793) Evening. War ships of the blue squadron at anchor, sign. and dated l.r.: 'D. Serres 1789'

Oil on wood

Three British warships of the Blue Squadron (rear-guard in the battle line) lie on a roadstead. The flagship in the middle, a Third Rate ship-of-the-line, is flying a blue pennant on the main mast. This indicates the presence of the admiral. To the right side, in the background, a Second Rate ship-of-the-line and a frigate are riding at anchor. Long-boats and jolly-boats are ferrying crew members ashore.

Thomas Luny (1759–1837) A Mediterranean port,

sign. and dated l.l.: 'Luny 1823' Oil on canvas

Thomas Luny was born in the southern English county of Cornwall. At the age of eleven, he went to London and became a pupil of Francis Holman (mentioned 1767–1790). Luny specialised in maritime themes and exhibited at the Royal Academy. The British East India Company was one of his regular customers. In 1807, he moved to Teignmouth on the south coast of England. By that time, Luny was already suffering from an inflammatory arthropathy. Subsequently, this led him to being wheelchair bound and he was unable to use his fingers. But this did not stop him from painting: He gripped the brush between the palms of his hands or tied it to his wrist. He still earned his living with commissioned works: He painted naval battles, coastal scenes and the surrounding countryside. Thomas Luny died in Teignmouth in 1837.

Montague Dawson (1895–1973) Onward the 'Lightning', clipper 'Lightning';

sign. l.l.: 'Montague Dawson' Oil on canvas Montague Dawson was born in Chiswick, London. During the First World war, he served as an officer in the Royal Navy serving on destroyers and minesweepers. Dawson was a passionate artist and rarely had his pencil out of his hand, even on anti-submarine patrol. After his retirement from the Navy, painting became his profession. He devoted himself to the depiction of offshore sailing and historical events, but also picked up on contemporary naval motifs. During the Second World War, he worked as a war artist capturing many British and American naval actions on canvas. The clippers were his favourite subject, and this fast sailing ship can be found in his paintings more frequently than any other subject. The boom in maritime trade at the beginning of the 19th century necessitated faster ships for more travel. The square-rigged clipper ship

Highlight:
Dawson
(1895–1973)
Onward the
'Lightning'

had a fine-lined hull. And one of the main features of the clipper was its protruding bow, which added to the streamlined appearance of the hull and was adopted to comply with existing measurement rules. The American shipyard of Donald McKay built a large number of famous clipper ships at East Boston. 'Lightning' was one of them (1854). She ran at 18 kn, i.e. 33.3 km/h – a record performance.

Barry Mason (born 1947) The white ship.

sign. l.l.: 'Barry Mason' Oil on canvas
Barry Mason was born in Seaton on the south coast of England, where he still lives and works. He studied painting at the Exeter College of Art. Later, he specialised in marine painting. His favourite topics include River Thames scenes, sea battles and historical ships. With 'A London dock shortly before the First World War', the artist describes his subject on the back of the picture. 'On a square-rigged sailing ship with steel hull the sails hang out to dry. She is ready to be hauled to her berth and tugs are standing by. All around, loading and unloading of vessels continues.'
As a unifying motif, rust turns up everywhere: It is both a symbol for transcience and an expression for melancholic romance. The sailing ship stands for the era of the 'Windjammers', that gradually came to an end.

Highlight:
'The White ship' by Barry Mason
– a harbour image filled with melancholic romance

A report about the sea – naval war correspondents

What would we know today of past events at sea, had there not been marine painters on board? For example: in 1801, a naval battle is raging off Copenhagen. A British naval unit under the command of Admiral Hyde-Parker and Lord Nelson is about to defeat the Danish fleet. Robinson Kittoe, a marine painter, is sitting on deck of HMS 'Defiance'. A sketchbook is resting on his knees. Kittoe sketches obsessively, despite the fact that there is fighting all around him. He is a commissioned painter. His task is to capture all events on canvas. He is a reporter, a chronicler. Large scale paintings and graphics will later on be the result of his work.

Kittoe's book, filled with his sketches, can be seen in the exhibition, along with coloured engravings of the 'Battle of Copenhagen' by Nicholas Pocock (1740–1821), based on Kittoe's drawings.

This tradition has continued in the Royal Navy: Marine painters could be found aboard British warships during the Falklands war in 1982.

In France too, there still exist the 'Peintres officiels de la Marine', the Official Painters of the Navy: 40 selected artists belong to this traditional French artists' association, which also includes a military rank on admission – their trademark: an anchor as part of their signature.

But not only artistic impressions of warlike operations do provide us with information about seafaring and naval history: There is much about shipbuilding and ship types and their distribution and development within the last 400 years that we would never have known without the existence of marine painters.

WATERCOLOURS, UNITED KINGDOM

Frank William Scarbrough (1860–1939)
Erith Reach, London

The Thames at Erith: Erith Reach, London sign. l. r.: 'F. W. Scarbrough' Watercolour Frank William Scarbrough lived and worked in London, since 1901 he resided in Lincoln. He became known mainly for his atmospheric portrayals of maritime traffic on the River Thames in Greater London. He exhibited his works from 1890 to 1939. This watercolour depicts merchant ships, barges and tugs on the River Thames at Erith. At the end of the 19th century, Erith was a small industrial town east of London, today it belongs to the London Borough of Bexley.

Derek G. M. Gardner (1914–2007)
The U.S.S. 'Franklin reached Spithead roadstead in 1818, sign. and dated l. r.:
'Derek G. M. Gardner 1986' Watercolour Derek George Montague Gardner was born in Buckinghamshire in the South East of England. His father held the position of 'Chief Engineer of the Clyde', being responsible for the safety of the large passenger liners of the Cunard shipping company after launching until their trial trips. His father's work influenced Gardner's own

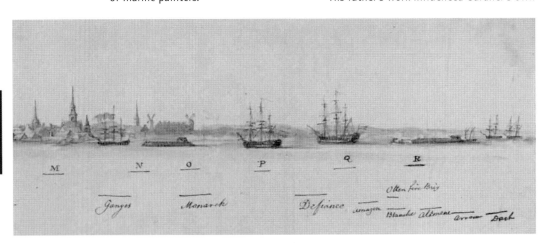

Sketch book: The Battle of Copenhagen, 2. April 1801 Artist: Robinson Kittoe

activity as an engineer and his lifelong interest in boats. During the Second World War he served in the Royal Navy, and later worked as an engineer in the colonial service in Kenya. During his years in Africa, he learned to paint. In 1963, he returned to England and began a career as a marine painter. In 1966, he became a member of the Royal Society of Marine Artists, who in 1988, appointed him Honorary Vice President for life. Derek Gardner died on February 11, 2007.

The foreground of this picture is dominated by the American frigate U.S.S. 'Franklin'. This two-decker was built in 1815 at Humphreys & Penrose, Philadelphia Navy Yard, and was equipped with 74 cannons. In November 1817, U.S.S. 'Franklin' carried the new American ambassador, Richard Rush, to Britain. It is possible that this mission forms the historical background for Derek Gardner's picture. Until 1820 the frigate was the flagship of the Mediterranean fleet of the U.S. Navy.

SCANDINAVIA

Anton Melbye (1818–1875)
Sailing ships
sign. and dated l.l.: 'Anton Melbye 1859'
Oil on canvas
Anton Melbye, born in Copenhagen, is considered for many to be the most important Danish marine painter. He first studied shipbuilding, then in 1838 attended the Copenhagen Academy of arts. In 1840, Melbye exhibited in Charlottenborg

for the first time. He died in Paris. The offshoot of a low pressure zone are visible on the left side of the painting. There is a clear, wide view behind this. A strong wind blows towards the shore against a rocky cliff, in front of which a sailing boat pushes through the turbulent sea. The Danish brig sails high on the wind. Smaller vessels sail against the wind to the coast. In the background, on the right, a further brig can be seen.

Vilhelm Melbye (1824–1882)
After the storm
sign. and dated l.l.: 'W. Melbye 1873'
Oil on canvas
Vilhelm Melbye, born in Helsingør, studied at the Art Academy in Copenhagen as a student of his brother Anton. Already in his lifetime, he received praise for his dramatic scenes, set in romantic style: A de-masted bark, disabled, languishes in the waves. Her jib boom is broken; only stumps remain of the foremast and main mast. The rod is missing from the mizzen mast, a flag with the Dutch colours had been fixed to it. Some of the ropes hang overboard, a yardarm lies diagonally across the bow. In the remnants of the sunset, a square rigger can be seen in the distance on the horizon: hope of salvation for the crew.

Christian Ferdinand Andreas Molsted (1862–1930) Visit of the Danish King Christian V. to the 'Christianus Quintus'
sign. and dated l.r.: 'Chr. Molsted 96',
oil on canvas
Christian Ferdinand Andreas Molsted was born in Draw on the island of Amager, near Copenhagen, where he died in 1930. Molsted received his training at the Royal

Danish Academy of Art. He painted both contemporary as well as historical maritime themes and worked as an illustrator.

The historical background of the painting: During the Scanian war (1674–1679), on July 12th 1677, the Danish King Christian V visited the 'Christianus Quintus', a warship that was named after him. On the previous day, a naval action had taken place in Karge Bay between the Danish and Swedish. The Danish fleet had been victorious.

INTERNATIONAL/GERMANY

Robert Charles Gustave Laurens Mols (1848–1903)
Antwerp

sign. l.l.: 'Robert Mols' Oil on wood
The Belgian landscape and marine painter Robert Charles Gustave Laurens Mols was born in Antwerp in 1848. He studied at the Antwerp Academy and in 1866 studied with Jean François Millet (1814–1875) in Paris. Since 1863 Mols exhibited in his hometown. His paintings were also shown in the Paris Salon, in Berlin and at the world exhibitions in Paris (1889) and Antwerp (1894). Robert Mols died in 1903, in the city where he had spent most of his life and which was repeatedly the subject and setting of his paintings.

This painting depicts a port basin in Antwerp in the second half of the 19th century. Like a guard of honour ships are moored in the basin. Lit by the sun, a large building

is representative of the town. In the shade, however, are the ship's hulls on the right mole: looking at their dark contourless colours they seem to merge. The artist used colours only slightly more intensive to depict the ship's hulls moored on the left mole. A maze of masts, spars, sails, and ropes surmount the scenery. It is not the individual ships that are the subject of the painting, they are depicted as part of a mass. The close connection of the large international port with the city is emphasised.

Franklin D. Briscoe (1844–1903) Breezy Northern New York Bay

sign. and dated l.r.: 'F. D. Briscoe 1874'
Oil on canvas

Franklin Dullin Briscoe was born in Baltimore in the US State of Maryland and died in Philadelphia, Pennsylvania. Briscoe was a student of Edward Moran (1829–1901). Even though he sometimes depicted other themes, he is known today mainly as a marine painter.

In the foreground, there are fishermen in two boats, bringing in their nets in the churning sea.

Johannes Holst (1880–1965) Seascape

sign. and dated u.l.: 'Joh's Holst 1913'
Oil on canvas
Marine painters were the 'reporters of the sea' for centuries: After the invention of photography, cameras largely took over the task of documentation. Many artists were looking for new challenges; some, for example, focussed exclusively on the elements. This is an explanation for artists venturing to paint water of the sea in all its manifestations and moods during the last 100 years.

Depicting an accurate image of the interaction of water, wind and clouds on canvas, where nothing distracts from the elements, is one of the most difficult challenges faced by an artist. The painter Johannes Holst is one of the masters of this art. Johannes Holst was born on 22 Octo-

ber 1880, in Altenwerder near Hamburg. He had an early interest in painting, and initially opted for training as a decorative artist. The master craftsmen Julius and Hinrich Lüdders were also well-known ship portrait painters, and so they became his tutors in two respects. In his paintings, Holst aimed to uncover the real appearance of things. He was fascinated by the tall ships of yesteryear as well as large passenger steamers, trawlers and sailing barges – and time and again the sea itself. Above all, it was the depiction of the moving sea and stormy skies, which was characteristic of Holst's work. Johannes Holst died on 3 July 1965 in his house in Altenwerder.

CAPTAIN'S PAINTINGS

Captain's paintings (19 century/early 20 century)

The detailed and faithfully reproduced image of a ship is at the heart of this type of painting. The main customers for these paintings were mostly the captains – hence the term. The first paintings in this genre were probably from the middle of the 18th century in Italy. Their history continued until the early 20th century, when they finally fell out of fashion and were ousted by photography.

The golden age of captain's paintings was in the 19th century. In all major ports of the world, painters specialised in these portraits. Most of them were self-taught and had no artistic training. They made technically correct representations of ships, often with the aid of sailing trips and rigging plans of models. A ship in profile is the characteristic motif of these paintings. Sometimes there are coastlines or ports in the background. Often the names of the vessel depicted and its master can be found at the bottom of the painting.

Edouard Adam (1847–1929) The British commercial steamer 'Anne Thomas', Captain's painting

sign. and dated l.r.: 'Edw. Adam 1894' Attributed to Edouard Adam
Oil on canvas

Edouard Adam lived and worked in the French seaport of Le Havre. Alongside John Henry Mohrmann and Antonio Jacobsen, he was one of the most important ship portrait artists at the turn of the last century. He probably painted over 1,500 pictures, their central motif mostly is a steamship. 'Anne Thomas' was built in 1883 at Palmer's in Newcastle, UK. The ship's home port was Cardiff on the south coast of Wales.

John Henry Mohrmann (1857–1916)
Steamer 'Marxburg' on the River Schelde
near Antwerp, Captain's painting
sign. and dated l.r.: 'H. Mohrmann 1897'
Oil on wood
John Henry Mohrmann was born in San
Francisco, and went to sea at the age of 13.
He later worked as a theatre painter in Kassel
and as a restorer in England. In 1884, he settled in Antwerp as a ship portrait painter. The
steamer 'Marxburg' was built in 1891 at Hels-
ingor/Denmark for the Deutsche Dampfschifffahrts-Gesellschaft Hansa in Bremen.

Hans von Petersen (1850–1914)
Sketchbook (original + touchscreen)
97 pages of impressive sketches by the marine painter Hans von Petersen. It is filled
with detailed pencil drawings and watercolour paintings. Some pencil sketches
contain colour information – reminders for
the subsequent colouring with watercolours
and opaque white. The pictured ships such
as Hamburg harbour barges and tugs or
trawlers and cargo barges from the North
Sea coast and lower Elbe area, suggest that
the studies are from the 1890s, from one or
two of his longer stays in Hamburg. Hans
Petersen was born in Husum. We only have
fragmented knowledge of his career before
he moved to Munich in 1886. In 1885,
along with fellow artists, he began working
on the 'Panorama of German colonies'. In
the late 19th century there was demand for
the creation of panorama buildings, such as

the Crystal Palace in Leipzig or the Munich
panorama building at Theresienhöhe. Petersen then worked more and more on large
panoramic scenes.
Petersen was a very well-known and
highly sought-after artist in his lifetime.
His paintings were shown at numerous
exhibitions at home and abroad. In 1902,
he was awarded the Knight's Cross of the
Order of merit of the Bavarian Crown. Thus
he was elevated to the level of nobility and
received the addition to his name 'Knight
of': Hans Ritter von Petersen died on June
18, 1914, in his office in the Munich Glass
Palace, by committing suicide. He suffered
from depression and an eye disease, which
would have resulted in his blindness. During
the 20th century, Hans Ritter von Petersen
was almost entirely forgotten. It was only
in 2010/11 in the Upper Bavarian region of
Fürstenfeldbruck and in his home city of
Husum that exhibitions of his life and his
work were once again promoted.

GERMANY

Late success: German marine painting
in the 19th and 20th centuries
From the middle of the 19th century, the
marine painting genre also was also established in Germany. The depiction of a sea
storm off the Norwegian coast (1837) and
the collision of a paddle steamer with an
iceberg (1981) brought renown to Andreas
Achenbach (1815–1910), who is often referred to as the 'Father' of German marine
painting, although his paintings were not
only restricted to maritime themes.
The real success story of the genre started
with Kaiser Wilhelm II – his 'love of the sea
and the navy', and his quest, as he formu-
lated in his memoirs, for naval supremacy.
Wilhelm II supported marine painting, and
in particular, his favourite painters Carl
Saltzmann (1847–1923), Hans Bohrdt
(1857–1945) and Willy Stöwer (1864–
1931). To support German fleet policy with
art they regarded as their most noble task.

'Literature and art were consciously or unconsciously to serve the interests of the fatherland; with their oeuvre they were to promote the understanding of maritime issues to the public', Hans Bohrdt wrote. These three artists often accompanied their patron Emperor Wilhelm II on board the 'Hohenzollern'. Immediately after the end of the First World War, times were difficult for marine painters. The Imperial promotion ceased, and support from the press waned. Apart from historical themes, their field of activity became severely restricted. It was not until the revival of merchant shipping in the 1920s that the situation improved, and with the rearmament in 1935 as a result of the German–British fleet agreement, the Navy once again provided rewarding motifs.

Robert Parlow (1835–1901) Kaiser Wilhelm II. On board the ice-breaker 'Berlin'

sign. and dated l.l.: 'Rob. Parlow 1891, Stettin', Oil on canvas
Robert Parlow was born in Stepenitz in Brandenburg as son of a bargeman, and initially he also worked as a bargeman. In 1870, he gave up this profession to devote himself to painting. He studied for four years at the Berlin School of Art. He then returned to his hometown, later living and working in Stettin. Kaiser Wilhelm II acquired two of his paintings.
Historical background to the painting:
The icebreakers 'Berlin', 'Stettin' and 'Swinemünde' broke up the frozen fairway between Swinemünde and Stettin in January 1891. Kaiser Wilhelm II. was on board the 'Berlin', his flag flying in the masthead. The three icebreakers were built at the Stettiner Vulkan shipyard and completed in 1888 resp. 1889.

Hans Bohrdt (1857–1945) Fort Wadsworth

sign. and dated l. r.: 'Hans Bohrdt 84'
Oil on canvas
Hans Bohrdt was born on February 11th 1857 in Berlin. He learned to paint by himself. His greatest patron was Kaiser Wilhelm II. From the monarch's point of view, Bohrdt was one of those marine painters who translated his fleet policy into art best (the others were Willy Stöwer and Carl Saltzmann). Hans Bohrdt frequently accompanied the Emperor on his 'Nordland' travels and on fleet manoeuvres. Bohrdt's preferred topics were coastal landscapes, ports and ships. The Kunstverein Hamburg exhibited his works in 1895, 1902 and 1906. Hans Bohrdt died in Berlin in 1945. Fort Wadsworth on Staten Island is one of the oldest military installations in the United States and has protected New York City for almost 200 years. Since 1995, it has been part of a public recreational park.

Carl Saltzmann (1847–1923) Beach view of waves and sea spray

sign. l. r.: 'Saltzmann Ddf', Oil on canvas
Carl Saltzmann was born on September 23, 1847 in Berlin. Initially a pupil of Berlin marine painter Hermann Eschke (1823–1900), he later attended the Düsseldorf Academy. Wilhelm I bought his first large painting; he taught painting to princes Wilhelm (later Kaiser Wilhelm II) and Heinrich. In 1894, Saltzmann became a lecturer and, in 1896, a Professor at the Berlin Academy. The landscape and marine painter died on 14 January 1923 in Potsdam.

Andreas Achenbach (1815–1910) Incoming fishing boats

sign. and dated l. r.: 'A. Achenbach 88' Oil on canvas
Born on September 29th 1815 in Kassel as a son of a merchant, Andreas Achenbach began his education at the Art Academy in Düsseldorf at the early age of twelve. He studied in St. Petersburg in the late 1820s.

> **Highlight:** 'Incoming fishing boats' by Andreas Achenbach. The 1805-born painter was a pioneer and role model for German maritime painting.

The artistic traditions of Dutch landscape painting left a long-lasting impression on him.

Andreas Achenbach is considered to be one of the most important representatives of the Düsseldorf School of painting. Precise observation of nature, without topography, is typical for him. Although he never devoted himself exclusively to marine painting, in Germany he was considered to be the pioneer and model for this genre. The artist died in Düsseldorf on 1 April 1910.

'Incoming fishing boats' portrays sailing boats, and in the background, a paddle steamer guiding ships to a safe haven in choppy seas. Only a narrow access is available for them between the flooded bulwark at the right edge of the picture and debris floating dangerously close in the foreground.

Claus Bergen (1885–1964) Barque with storm sails

sign. and dated l. r.: 'Claus Bergen 1926'
Gouache

Claus Bergen was born in Stuttgart. His father, Fritz Bergen (1857–1941), was a popular painter and illustrator in Imperial Germany. Claus studied at the Munich Academy. Before he turned to marine painting, he made a name for himself as an illustrator for the adventure novels of Karl May. In the First World War, he worked as an artist with the High Seas Fleet. He became the official painter of the Battle of Jutland even though he didn't participate. In the Second World War he was the official painter of the German U-Boat fleet. In addition to his paintings of naval battles and warships, Claus Bergen left behind pictures of luxury liners from the 1920s as well as numerous seascapes. He died in 1964 in Lenggries, Bavaria.

Carl Wilhelm Hugo Schnars-Alquist (1855–1939) HAPAG passenger steamer of the 'Imperator class'

sign. l. l.: 'Schnars-Alquist, Hamburg', Oil on canvas
As the son of a Hamburg merchant family, Carl Wilh. Hugo Schnars-Alquist initial-

ly became a businessman himself. After deciding to make painting his profession, he travelled to Berlin in 1886. He studied at the Berliner Akademie, where he later taught as a professor. In 1898 he moved back to Hamburg, where he died in 1939. Schnars-Alquist freqently went on sea voyages. He became acquainted with all facets of the sea which were portrayed in his paintings in great detail. In addition Schnars-Alquist painted several pictures for the interior decoration of passenger steamers of the Hamburg-Amerika Line, i.e. for the first class dining-room of the 'Imperator', built in 1913. At that time she was the largest ship in the world.

The illustration shows one of the three passenger steamers of the Imperator-class, which were built in Hamburg for HAPAG. The 'Imperator' was first of class and was built at A. G. Vulcan. Her sister ships were the passenger liners 'Vaterland' (1914) and 'Bismarck' (1922) built at Blohm & Voss. The 'Vaterland' is still the largest passenger ship that ever flew the German flag. During the First World War, the 'Vaterland' (later 'Leviathan', United States Line) was confiscated by the USA; after the First World War the 'Imperator' (later 'Berengaria', Cunard Line) and 'Bismarck' (later 'Majestic', White Star Line) were handed over to Great Britain.

Albert Schindehütte (born 1939)
'...to new shores'
Woodcut, 193.5 x 334 cm
Albert Schindehütte was born in Kassel and grew up in Breitenbach, today Schauenburg district. From 1956 to 1959 he studied at the Werkkunstschule Kassel. In 1962 he moved to Berlin. In 1963 he was one of the founders of the Rixdorfer Drucke workshop. Since then, he has created a massive body of artistic work, especially drawings, etchings, woodcuts and lithography.

The woodcut '... to new shores' from 2007/08, which was created by manual abrasion on size 345 x 204 cm paper and printed, is probably the largest wooden pressure print ever produced in one piece.

The title refers to the naturalist and explorer Hans Staden of Wolfhagen in Northern Hesse, who wrote the first detailed report on Brazil in 1557 (The hand print presented to the International Maritime Museum in Hamburg was donated by the MACS Maritime Carrier Shipping GmbH et co Hamburg shipping line).

Friedrich Kallmorgen (1856–1924) The port of Hamburg
sign. and dated l. r.: 'Fr. Kallmorgen 1906'
Oil on canvas
Friedrich Kallmorgen, born 15 November 1856, came from a family of architects in Hamburg. He initially went to the Düsseldorf Academy, then transferred to the Karl-

sruhe Academy in 1877 and was a student of Hans Frederic Gude (1825–1903). In 1888 he moved to Grötzingen and became the co-founder of the Grötzingen painter's colony. From 1902 to 1918, he taught as a professor at the Berlin Academy. In 1899, he rented an apartment in Hamburg Hafenstrasse, from where he could watch life go by on the River Elbe. Since 1910 he devoted most of his creative power to become the 'painter of the port of Hamburg'. Kallmorgen died on 2 June 1924. The 1906 painting depicts the Norderelbe with views eastward. Blurred in the distance is the Elbe railway bridge.

INTERNATIONAL/GERMANY

John Atkinson Grimshaw (1836–1893) Thames Embankment at night
sign. l. r.: 'Atkinson Grimshaw' Oil on wood
The British artist John Atkinson Grimshaw was influenced by the pre-Raphaelites, who held a circle in his home town of Leeds. He specialised in landscape painting and genre scenes, later on urban scenes at night. In 1880, he rented a studio in London and painted views of the city. From 1874 to 1885 he exhibited at the Royal Academy. This painting depicts the south-

Themistocles von Eckenbrecher (1842–1921) In the eternal ice near Spitsbergen
sign. and dated l.l.: 'T. v. Eckenbrecher 1908', titled: l. r. Oil on canvas
Themistocles von Eckenbrecher was born in Athens in 1842. He spent his youth in Constantinople then moved to Germany in 1858. From 1861 to 1867, he lived in Düsseldorf, and for three years he was a private student of Oswald Achenbach (1827–1905). As international tourism began to discover Scandinavia in the 1880s, he served the growing market for coastal views and motifs of this region. In 1889 he moved to Berlin. The passenger steamer 'Oihonna' was built in 1898 by Gourley Bros. & co., Dundee (Scotland) and ran for the Suomen Höyrylaiva Osakeyhtiö (Finnish Steamship A.G.), Helsinki.

ern embankment along the River Thames in the centre of London, overlooking the city. In the background, on the left: St. Paul's Cathedral.

Karl Schmidt-Rottluff (1884–1976)
Sierksdorfer Bay
sign. l. r.: 'S. Rottluff;' Oil on chalk
Karl Schmidt-Rottluff (actually Karl Schmidt) was born in Rottluff near Chem-

nitz. This painter and graphic artist is one of the most important representatives of Expressionism and was a founding member of the famous group 'Die Brücke' (The Bridge): Emil Nolde was also briefly a member of the 'Bridge': During a visit with Nolde on the Danish island of Alsen, Schmidt-Rottluff discovered the sea and its typical landscape as an artistic theme. The artist died in Berlin.

The old fishing village and present day seaside resort of Sierksdorf is situated on the Bay of Lübeck. Between 1951 and 1973 Karl Schmidt-Rottluff spent every summer in Sierksdorf.

2 TREASURE CHAMBER

Gold model of the 'Santa Maria'.
Pure gold, coin gold, red, yellow and pale gold, ropes (running rigging): Platinum, base plate: Sodalite. Manufacturer: H.J. Wilm, Hamburg, 1992
The 'Santa Maria' was the flagship of Christopher Columbus when he discovered America in 1492.
This model, made in 1992, is the only model ship in the world made of gold and built in authentic manner along the plank-on-frame method.

Uwe Lütgen (born 1944)
'Meteor III'

sign. and dated l. l. 'Uwe Lütgen 03' (in mirror writing) Reverse painting on glass
Uwe Lütgen has a long-standing passion for classic sailing yachts. His paintings convey liveliness and a strong plasticity. 'Meteor III' appears to be within easy reach.
Kaiser Wilhelm II commissioned his third 'Meteor' from the United States. The schooner was built in 1902 by the Townsend & Downey Shipbuilding Corp. on Shooters Island near New York. In addition to the owner's cabin and guest rooms, she had a dining parlour for 24 persons, a kitchen for their lordship and one for the crew and several bathrooms. Although, over the years, its heavy hull construction was an increasing disadvantage concerning sailing regattas, the Emperor sailed the schooner until 1909. Then the yacht changed owners several times. In 1947, her home port was Boston, according to Lloyd's register. Uwe Lütgen's atelier in the IMMH can be found next to the Treasure Chamber.

Silver table centrepiece with sailing yachts.

A silver table centrepiece shows cutters and yachts owned and steered by Prince Henry of Prussia, the brother of Wilhelm II, during his long sailing career. This beautiful piece of work is a gift from the Imperial Yacht Club, Kiel, to the Prince and his wife on the occasion of their silver wedding anniversary on 24 May 1913. Kaiser Wilhelm II was commodore of the KYC.

Model ships from amber

Model ships made of natural amber – of exceptional quality and extremely rare and valuable. The three models displayed here were made by the amber sculptor Alfred Schlegge, who was born in Königsberg in 1923 and who, amongst other things, worked for the governmental amber factory in his hometown. The rigging of the ship models is made of 14 karat gold threat. The experienced amber sculptor created the light curves, e.g. the sails, by slightly heating the material to make it malleable. Alfred Schlegge specialised in the production of historic sailing ships. In 2003, the Preußen Museum in Minden arranged for the exhibition 'Treasures of Nordic Gold' in his honour:

Frigate 'Hollandia'

Model made of natural amber, rigging made of gold. Model maker: Alfred Schlegge

Model ships of natural amber are precious rarities. This model is a replica of the 1660-built 'Hollandia', a 80 gun two-decker. She was the flagship of Admiral Tromp in the so-called Four Day's Battle in June 1666 during the Second Anglo-Dutch War. The transom and the fore-topsail show the coat-of-arms of the House of Orange with the motto of the Order of the Garter: 'Hon[n]i Soit Qui Mal y Pense' (May he be shamed who thinks badly of it).

Ship-of-the-line

Painted wood, beginning of the 19[th] century
Crafted by prisoners of war
The model of a warship armed with 80 guns originates from the time of the French revolutionary and Napoleonic wars.

It was built by French prisoners of war who were interned in England. The detailing of the decks and the equipment inside the hull as well as the outside fittings of the ship-of-the-line are amazing.

Letter from Vice Admiral Horatio Nelson to Captain Staines April 6th 1805,

written on board the 'Victory'.
Victory, April 6th 1805
'Dear Staines,
I wish I could avoid sending home your rotten Camelion, but I can do nothing else. Let us hope I shall take the French fleet before you go and then very probably you will find another ship. Sir Richard Bickerton is as well disposed to serve you as your Red Line friend Nelson Bronte
You must forgive a short letter. I will if you do go send you a letter to Lord Melville.
Capt.t Staines'.

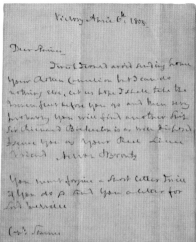

Persons mentioned:
Lord Horatio Nelson (1758–1805), 1801 Vice Admiral, 1803 Commander-in-Chief of the British fleet in the Mediterranean. On October 21st 1805, Nelson died during the Battle of Trafalgar.
Sir Richard Bickerton (1759–1832), Vice Admiral under Nelson, Admiral of the Red
Sir Thomas Staines (1776–1830), Naval officer
Robert Dundas, Viscount Melville (1771–1851), British statesman

Porcelain of vessels of the Imperial German Navy

This chinaware was used solely in the officer's mess. Some porcelain shows the ship's name printed on a meandering blue ribbon.

Dutch wine balloons

Glass, hand-painted, probably early 19th century. On each of the two bottles, a famous event of Dutch naval history is shown: the capturing of the English Admiral vessel 'Royal Charles' during the so-called 'Battle of the

Medway' in June 1667 (above) and a scene from the famous battle of Camperdown (Dutch: Camperduin) off the Dutch coast on 11 October 1797 (below).

Lyonel Feininger (1871–1956) Fishing trawler

sign. l.l.: 'Feininger, dated l.r.: '33' Watercolour

Lyonel Feininger was born on 17 July 1871 in New York City. In 1887 he travelled to Germany to study. He attended the art school in Hamburg, as well as the Academy in Berlin, and also studied for some time in Paris. Cubism had a decisive influence on his work.

Feininger soon developed his own style, which was characterised by prismatic and broken and at the same time sharp areas of colour and crossing and intersecting streaks. After the First World War, Feininger taught graphics at Bauhaus. Banned by the National Socialists, he returned to the United States in 1936. He died in New York on 13 January 1956. Feininger often used the subject of a solitary vessel on open water. Here, as stated at the bottom of the painting, the motif is a 'fishing trawler'. He observes his subject as if he is looking through a crystal, and inserts it into a crystalline structure. It has the effect of being peculiarly rigid; it is visible, yet seems to be out of reach and other-worldly.

3 BONE SHIPS

In this section you will find the world's largest private collection of bone ships. Bone ships ('prisoner-of-war model ships') were produced during the Coalition and Napoleonic wars (1792–1807/1808–1812) mainly by French prisoners of war. They constructed them from the bones left over from their food rations. The prisoners were interned on unrigged sailing ships, called hulks, which were anchored along the south coast of England and in the Thames. From 1803 to 1814, 122,400 captured French soldiers were brought to England. On the prison hulks room didn't suffice anymore to house them. Hence, prison camps were erected in the coun-

tryside, amongst others at Norman Cross and Dartmore. All of these places had very poor living conditions: everything was cramped, food was lousy.

The model ships were made mainly from bleached and dried beef and mutton bone. These small works of art were used as bargaining chips, for example to supplement food rations. Later, English masters also 'ordered' their ships: The work was carried out with much imagination, because work could not be carried out according to a plan. Usually several prisoners worked together, each specialising in a particular aspect. Very few of the artists are known by name.

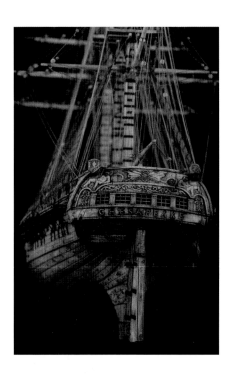

USS 'Chesapeake', frigate

Model from darkened whale bones, 'Prisoner of War' model

USS 'Chesapeake', a 46 gun frigate, had been launched in 1799 at Norfolk, Virginia. In June 1813, during the Anglo-American War, she was captured by the English frigate 'Shannon'. The brief encounter lasted for only 15 minutes. The American commander was killed; the crew was captured. During their captivity, the crew built a scale model of their former vessel for the captain's widow. The model of the 'Chesapeake' is probably the largest bone ship ever built.

The model of a 64-gun two-decker ship-of-the-line, was built at a scale of about 1:500 and stands in a box decorated with inlays made of straw. In order to show the other side of the model, a mirror was used on the inner side of the rear wall.

English three-decker First Rate ship-of-the-line
Bone ship, 'Prisoner of War' model
The model of a 108 gun First Rate ship-of-the-line, richly decorated with an inlaid baseplate under a glass hood. The model for this beautiful and extremely precise crafted bone ship model may have been HMS 'Victory' (104 guns), launched in 1765 at Chatham. She was Nelson's flagship at Trafalgar in 1805.

Third Rate ship-of-the-line
Bone ship, 'Prisoner of War' model

English Navy cutter
Bone ship, 'Prisoner of War' model
The smallest armed vehicle under sail was the cutter. Designed and built in England in the mid-18th century, the cutter was used mainly for police and customs tasks like hunting for smugglers. In narrow coastal waters their fast and effective boats were superior to every other ship of the Royal Navy. Despite their stolid appearance, cutters were fast and agile. They were ideally adapted to the waters around the British Isles with their short, hard waves.

Highlight: Bone ships – a worldwide unique collection. These delicately crafted models were made by prisoners of war in England, during the French revolutionary and Napoleonic wars.

The classic material for model shipbuilding is wood, preferably boxwood or pear. Bone is much more difficult to craft; the preparation of the material is extremely

Prisoners of war carving bone ships aboard an English prison hulk during the French revolutionary and Napoleonic wars

Clarkson Frederick Stanfield (1793–1867)
Prisoner ships take prisoners on board,
Oil on wood

Clarkson Stanfield entered the British Merchant Navy at a young age; since 1808 he served in the Royal Navy. Due to an injury he left the Navy in 1814 and turned to scenography and panoramic painting as well as easel pictures and he participated in exhibitions. After he left from theatre he specialised in seascapes and depictions of coastal and river landscapes. Clarkson Stanfield is considered by many contemporary critics to be one of England's best marine and landscape painters.

The painting depicts two prison hulks in choppy sea and slightly hazy weather: Prison hulks were dismantled sailing ships used to house French prisoners of war during the French revolutionary and Napoleonic wars. Many of the famous bone ships were built on such ships. In the background, the observer can see fully occupied boats bringing the men on board. The boat in the foreground has apparently already unloaded its cargo.

time-consuming and painstaking. However, 20th-century model builders also carried out this craft – impressed by the work of prisoners of war from the Napoleonic wars.

Model ships from ivory

Ivory carving is a very old form of art. Its earliest evidence dates back 32,000 years. Ivory carvings have survived from Ancient Egypt, and in the form of ornaments and utensils made by the Greeks and Romans. We know of ivory carvings from early Christian art, and in the Middle Ages this craft was widespread and existed in almost every country and culture.

A new era in the history of ivory carving began with the discovery of the sea routes to India, now there was enough provisions of raw material. This craft then blossomed in the 17th century. The ship models presented here are crafted with great attention to detail. They were built mostly during the second half of the 20th century and are true-to-scale representations of historic sailing ships. And they are also rarities, because, for reasons of wildlife conservation, ivory is no longer available.

Full-rigged ship 'Charles W. Morgan'
Model in ivory

The whaler 'Charles W. Morgan' was built in 1841 at the Jethro and Zacharias Hillmann shipyard in New Bedford, Massachusetts. This was the era of the large American whaling fleets operating in particular from the New England states. 'Charles W. Morgan' is a full rigged ship of 40 metres length and 300 tons displacement. She is named after her owner, Charles Waln Morgan, and was

in service for 80 years. Since 1941, it has been on display as a museum ship at Mystic Seaport.
Scale 1:33, model maker: Leo Blümke

Galleons
Ship in a bottle; model in ivory
This ivory model depicts one of the famous 'race built galleons' of the English fleet that went to fight against the Spanish-Armada in 1588. The Galleon is armed with 28 guns.

4 LÜTGEN ATELIER

In his atelier on Deck 8, you can witness the famous maritime painter Uwe Lütgen 'live'!
Dates on the IMMH website.
Uwe Lütgen was born in Calau in Lower Lusatia, but came from an old Hamburg family. He made an apprenticeship as stage painter, afterwards he had the opportunity to undertake professional training as a

restorer at the Museum für Hamburgische Geschichte (now: Hamburg Museum). He began his artistic career restoring a painting by Hugo Schnars Alquist (1855–1939), whom he very much admires. The painting shows the schooner 'Hamburg' crossing the Atlantic; the customer was the North German Regatta Club. The club also requested him to make a copy of the painting. Besides Schnars-Alquist, Johannes Holst and Hans Bohrdt rank among the artists Uwe Lütgen very much appreciates. He refers to himself not as an artist but as a craftsman in the tradition of painters.
Uwe Lütgen is working as a freelance marine painter in Hamburg for more than thirty years. In addition to oil painting, he also has an interest in glass and porcelain painting. The main focus of his work is large-format oil paintings of yachts and race scenes, but in the tradition of historical marine painting. His paintings have found worldwide recognition and admiration.

Uwe Lütgen
at his atelier at
the IMMH

Prof. Peter Tamm received this ship modell at the age of six.
It was cast in lead. This gift was the starting point for the world's largest collection
of shipping and maritime history.

HIGHLIGHTS ON DECK 9

Wiking–Model of a coastal freighter –
the first model in the Peter Tamm collection.

Models by the Danish company Pilot,
located in Copenhagen are rarities.

Models of 'Von der Tann' and 'Königin Luise'
are unique items by Wiking in unusual scales.

The casting mould of the 'Warspite'
shows how models were cast in the 1930s.

These world championship models
bear witness to the high craftsmanship of the model maker.

The Dioramas of the Hamburg harbor
and the container terminal of Bremerhaven are rich in detail and get frequent updates.

Rare wooden miniature ships
demonstrate the desire to deliver quality work even under adverse circumstances.

Paper models –
craftsmanship on the highest level.

The passenger ship 'Sabino'
(1908) is one of the best models of the entire collection.

The model of the sidewheel tug 'Neptune' (1925)
represents an old boatmen's tradition on the Rhine. There is also historical film footage of a similar vessel on the deck.

Model of the survey ship 'Schaarhörn' (1908): The Schaarhörn is the first ship to be recorded in the Hamburg monument list. The quality of the model is impressive.

Historical diver's suit with helmet.
Heavy work under water was carried out in such suits.

THE BIG WORLD OF TINY SHIPS

This deck is devoted to models of the scale 1: 1,250. It is clear from a first glance that around 50,000 miniature models have plenty to offer.

The first example is a special one-off. This tiny model of a coaster is the first ship of the Tamm collection. Peter Tamm's interest in seafaring was triggered early on with this gift.

It is, like most of the models on this deck, at a scale of 1:1,250. This scale is derived from an altitude of 2,000 meters. From this height, real ships seem to have this very scale. In addition to single-ship models, Deck 9 also has fascinating displays of detailed dioramas depicting shipyards or port facilities.

An additional feature of this floor is that the model builders and their skills are appreciated. Partly individuals, and partly founders of well-known companies such as Pilot or Wiking. In addition to being cast in metal, ship models are also made of wood, paper or synthetic materials.

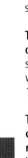

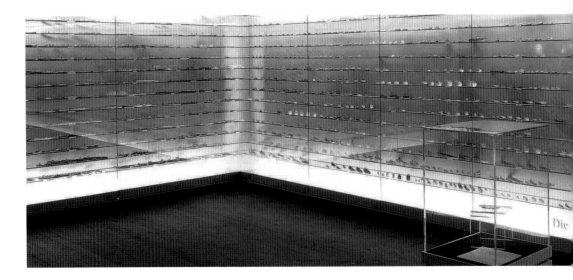

1 APPROXIMATELY 50,000 MODELS AT A SCALE OF 1: 1,250

are displayed on exhibition Deck 9. In the middle of the room, in a small display case, is the only five-centimetre-long model of a freighter. Peter Tamm was given this lead cast ship at the age of six. It was the starting point for the world's largest collection of maritime and naval history.

The miniature shipmodels are mainly collector's items today. Originally they were used as toys, and later for military purposes. Initially, the English scale of 1:1,200 was used, then later the scale was set at 1:1250. The reason: If you put such a model on the floor and look at it you see it the same way a fighter pilot would see the real ship from a flight altitude of 2,000 meters. During World War II such models have been used in Germany, Britain and the USA to train pilots for reconnaissance missions. Since the 1930s miniature shipmodels were cast in metal but during the 1940s due to a temporary shortage in metal plastic was used. Metal as a construction material allowed for a greater richness of detail. Today, waterline models on a miniature scale are collected all over the world. They represent the history of shipping from the beginning to the present day extremely well.

Displaycase full of ship miniatures
With its thousands of ship miniatures, the large display cases show a representative selection of merchant and navy vessels from around the world. The left hand side contains a great variety of merchant and passenger ships ordered according to country and shipping company. The right hand side contains international navy vessels.

On the rear side of the showcase all kinds of ships are put on display in a so called magazine manner to provide space for the museums many doublet and triplet miniature models.

Due to the uniform scale of all the models, size comparisons can be made. Two examples can demonstrate this: On the outside of another showcase, there is a bronze-age dugaout. At only one centimetre in length, it is one of the smallest models in this exhibition. To get an idea of its proportions now compare this tiny canoe with the 5-mast sailing ship to the left of it.

2 MANUFACTURERS

The creator of the waterline scale model is the naval historian Fred T. Jane. Born in 1865 in England, this expert had models of Royal Navy ships made of metal for the purpose of teaching naval tactics. They were ment to illustrate his lectures on strategy. By 1902, he already had over a hundred units in his portfolio. The models were initially very small. Later, Jane introduced a uniform scale of approximately 1:1,800 to improve the comparability of different ship types.

Fred T. Jane
The models were based on the sheer drawings of ships, which he first printed in 1898 in his fleet handbook 'All the World's Fighting ships'. This Almanac is still published annually. Apart from this major work and his 1909 handbook on aeroplanes and airships ('All the World's Airships') Jane has published a number of other books on maritime topics.

Highlight: Wiking-Model of a coastal freighter
The miniature was the first model in the Peter Tamm collection and the basis of his later collection.

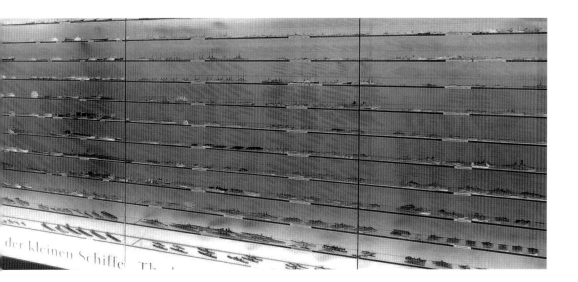

He quickly discovered that there was a great interest in such models from ship and navy enthusiasts, and founded a company which marketed his models in 1905. Manufacturers of pewter figures undertook the production. Very soon a wide range of Royal Navy ships was available. Fred T. Jane, who was regarded as a visionary and eccentric, died in 1916 at the age of 51. His work is continued today by Jane's Information Group, located in Coulsdon, Surrey. Annually, it publishes approximately 200 publications on all aspects of security and defence. The English toy manufacturer, Bas-

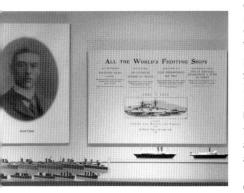

sett-Lowke, which established the uniform scale 1:1,200, is considered to be one of the first commercial manufacturers of waterline models. In 1911, the British Admiralty entered into a supply contract with Bassett-Lowke and used the models for training purposes. After the First World War, the company produced commercial ship models, which were sold on board passenger ships, as well as other places.

Pilot models and the Wiking company

Founded before 1930 in Denmark, the Pilot company was a long-time leader in the manufacture of waterline models. They worked closely with the German producer Wiking. From 1934, the two companies produced models of war and merchant ships by casting them in slate moulds and issued a joint sales catalogue.

In 1935, they switched towards using bronze moulds for casting and extended the programme to include railway, car and aircraft models. In addition models of ships and military technology in the scales of 1:200 and 1:1,250 made by Wiking were distributed. In parallel Pilot developed their own standard scale of 1:1000.

Pilot produced, in particular, models of civilian ships in the post-war period and cast most of the so-called veterans series for Wiking. Their sale came to an end in 1975. With the death of Henning Cortsen in 1974, the company dissolved. Wiking also ceased production of waterline models in 1975. During the course of its existence, Pilot produced around 420 ship models in series.

Highlight:
Models by the Danish company Pilot, Copenhagen, are rarities.

Naval war games

One display case exhibit navel-battle themed strategy games. One of them is the game Jutlandia – named after the great Battle of Jutland in 1916.

The game which is played using little metal models in a scale of 1:2,000 was launched in 1942 by Diego Rosada de la Espada in Mexico.

Battle Cruiser 'von der Tann',
Scale: 1:333

In 1938 Wiking-Modellbau received an order from the Museum for Oceanography in Berlin to build the Imperial German Navy in the scale of 1:333. The calculations necessary to do so were based on Erich Gröner's compendium 'German warships 1815–1936'. In 1943 this model series and other museum exhibits were stored away on a barge, due

Wiking:
Friedrich Karl Peltzer and his factory

At the beginning of the 1930s the model builder Friedrich Karl Peltzer (1903–1981) made his dream come true: He started to produce waterline models of merchantmen and warships in the scale of 1:1,250. Initially the son of an Imperial Navy officer produced his models based on britisch construction documents and thus adopted the common scale of 1:1,200 but later modyfied it to 1:1,250.

His first metal-cast models (at this time still with pinned turrets) were only reluctantly accepted by the toy trade. Only when his Berlin-based company introduced onto the market a model of a whole harbour with warehouses, piers, cranes and lighhouses the sales accelerated. Both the quality and the number of shiptypes availlable increased on an annual basis while the assortment got complemented with models of cars and aircrafts.

Soon, the navy and air force became aware of the models as they came in handy to train ship recognition and naval tactics.

Friedrich Karl Peltzer (1903–81)
The founder of Wiking-Modell-bau

to increasing air raid. The barge, however, received a bomb hit and the collection burned. Only the models 'von der Tann' and 'Derfflinger', which were still in production and had not yet been delivered, therefore survived the war.

Seaside resort ship 'Königin Luise'

Unique Wiking Model. In 1937 this model was manufactured for the HAPAG in the scale of 1:100.. Along with the artillery training ship 'Brummer', which has been missing since 1982, it is the only Wiking model in this scale. The company by then wantet to get into the buisness of producing and selling larger models. However there was no demand and the production was scrapped. The focus of the company remained the scale of 1:1,250.

'Warspite' casting mould

A preserved casting mould from Wiking is a rarity. The manufacturing process of the model in the 1930s began with a sketch. It was followed by a wooden master pattern, a bronze mould, a cast and finally the pinning of the turrets.

Seaside resort ship 'Königin Louise'
Wiking model, unique in scale 1:100

3 LOVE FOR DETAIL –
A SHIP MINIATURE IS CREATED

Choosing the Queen Mary 2 as an example we demonstrate the manufacturing proces of a miniature ship model in a selected showcase. The scale is 1:1,250.

The start of the process is always the desire to build a ship in miniature. A good documentation of the ship a model buildet intendes to make is crucial for a successful execution. For the most part images, photographs and drawings are used. In case of the Queen Mary 2 in this showcase even a real construction plan was availlable.

After studying these documents, the artist starts with the construction of a prototype of plastic plates. Using an elaborate process of cutting, carving, filing and gluing – around 1,100 handmade parts are produced and assembled. The process can take three months or longer, depending on size and details of the model. After the completion of the prototype, this is then launched into a mould where it is doused with an impression material (rubber). This is followed by a resting period, to allow the rubber to cure. Once that is done, a plaster dock is built around the rubber form and the original prototype enclosed within it. The plaster dock is necessary to be able to handle the form later during casting processes. After the plaster dock has dried out, the rubber form is extracted and the prototype is retrieved. The inner surface of the rubber block now has adopted the silhouette of the 'Queen Mary 2'. Then a connecting sprue is cut out, for the

subsequent casting. Now the Model can be cast in an alloy of tin and lead at 300° to 425° Celsius. After the metal has cooled, the plaster dock is set aside and the ships replica can be removed from the hot rubber mould. The mould, dependent on the level of detail, has a limited durability. Now the post-processing of the miniature begins, i.e. seperating the model from the sprue head, cleaning it and mounting of small parts that cannot be cast. Finally the miniature model gets painted by hand. The ship miniature of the 'Queen Mary 2', in perfect condition, can be seen positioned last in the cabinet. Almost all ship miniatures in the collection on Deck 9 are made of tin and are manufactured in the same way. Each ship miniature is a piece of art in its own right.

4 DIORAMAS OF SHIPPING AND
NAVAL HISTORY

At the rear of Deck 9 there are a number of large-scale dioramas. At the beginning reproductions of three most notable naval battles of british Admiral Horation Nelson are on display. His victories made him a legend in both Britain and abroad.

The Battle of the Nile
Napoleon's campaign in Egypt attempted i. a. to weaken the british supremacy in the Mediterranean. Initially Cairo was taken. But on 1 August 1798 a british fleet under the command of rear admiral Horatio Nelson utterly defeatet the anchoring french invasion fleet off the

nile estuary in a surprise attack from two sides. Of the thirteen French battleships, four were sunk, and nine were taken as prize. Nelson's naval victory strengthened the British position in the Mediterranean and isolated Napoleon's army in Egypt. Model maker: Dr. Hans Mehl

The Battle of Copenhagen

During the War of the Second Coalition (1798–1802) Russia, Sweden, Denmark, and Prussia insisted on a policy of armed neutrality towards the belligerent nations. When in 1800 the Russian Czar began to sympathize with Napoleon the British feared having to face a naval coalition of the baltic states joining forces with France. As a result a british fleet under Admiral Sir Hyde Parker with Horatio Nelson as second in command sailed into the baltic sea in early spring of 1801 to issue an ultimatum to the Danes demanding that they shoud give up on armed neutrality. The timing was favourable because by that time of the year the swedish and russian fleets were still blocked in their harbours by ice. When the Danes – as expected – rejected the

ultimatum, Nelson opened fire. Initially the british suffered significant losses so Hyde Parker gave Nelson a signal to retreat knowing that Nelson would continue the fight if he deemed it possible. And that is what Nelson did. He fought on until victory with the danish finally accepting a ceasefire. In the following negotiations they aggreed to give up the position of armed neutraliry. Model maker: Dr. Hans Mehl

The Battle of Trafalgar

On 21 October 1805 Horatio Nelson achieved his most notable victory. Toghether with his friend Vice Admiral Cuthbert Collingwood he defeatet a numerically superior franco-spanish fleet off Cape Trafalgar utilizing an unexpected tactic. Sailing in two columns, the English fleet broke at two points through the enemy line and destroyed numerous enemy ships after a turning manoeuvre. After

this seminal victory France ceased to be a major naval opponent for Britain. Nelson's death at the hands of a french sniper however overshadowed the triumph. His attack signal, England expects that every man will do his duty remains unforgotten. Model maker: Dr. Hans Mehl

Model of the Stülcken shipyard

H.C. Stülcken & Son shipyard at Steinwerder in Hamburg, located opposite of the Überseebrücke, was founded in 1845. The model shows the company around 1965, shortly before the takeover by Blohm + Voss. Model maker: Roland Klinger, Rodkling

5 DIORAMAS

Diorama of 'Kaiser-Wilhelm port', Hamburg

The warehouse 'Schuppen 74' and 'Schuppen 75' were the first new buildings in Hamburg after World War II. They were errected at the Kronprinzenkai in the Kaiser Wilhelm Harbour between 1947 and 1949. In the years that followed, vessels from Hapag, Norddeutscher Lloyd and various dutch shipping companies were unloaded here. Model maker: Klaus Kunath

Diorama of 'Imperial shipyard', Wilhelmshaven

In 1853, Prussia acquired a 313 hectare property by the river Jade from the Duchy of Oldenburg to establish a naval base. In 1864 constuction of a shipyard started and after the German-French war in 1870/71 the shipyard was named 'Imperial shipyard Wilhelmshaven'. Several battleships and torpedo boats were built here. The model shows the shipyard in 1915. Model maker: Wilhelm Thümler, Varel. Another yet smaller model shows the camouflaged battleship 'Tirpitz' at quai in the very same shipyard in 1940. Model maker: Roland Klinger

Diorama of the port of Hamburg

The port of Hamburg is Germany's largest sea port and a hub of international maritime transport. The model when completed will show the modern, western port of Moorburg up to the (opposite) Elbchaussee. It includes the Altenwerder and Waltershof container terminals, ore and coal handling of the Hansa port, car handling, grain loading and oil handling as well as the A7 motorway and the Elbe tunnel. The model is still under construction and is being completed step by step.

The cabinet measures 5.30 x 2.60 m.

The gantry cranes consist of 250 individual parts. There are currently (2015) 32,000 containers on view and their number will grow to 150,000. Model makers: Franz-Wilhelm Besch, Armin Flügge, Bernd Walsberg, scale 1: 1,250

Diorama Container terminal Bremerhaven

Another diorama in the back of Deck 9 is an eye catcher on its own right. The regularly updated model shows an exact representation of the container terminal facilities in Bremerhaven with the Nordschleuse lock and the village of Weddewarden. The impressive model was created in the scale of 1:1,250. There are a good 65,000 handmade and painted containers piled up in the miniature port. The construction of the scale model took several years. The depiction is superior in quality to aereal photography. Since the late 1960s, the container terminal 'Wilhelm Kaisen' has been expanded. At 4,980 metres, it is the longest riverside quay in the world today.

Data of the Terminal:
Quay length 4,980 m
Water depth 15.5 m
Total square metres 2.9 million square metres
Container bridges 35
Straddle carriers 198
Model builders: Franz Wilhelm Besch, Hans Küting, Hero Lang, Armin Flügge, Thomas Gatermann

Diorama 'Finger piers', New York

The diorama depicts so called 'finger piers' in the Hudson river on the west side of Manhattan. Piers like these are distinctive for New York City. The ones on view here were built in the 1930s under major La

Guardia for a new class of huge passenger ships en rout on the North Atlantic. The section from Pier 84 to Pier 94 became known throughout the world as 'luxury liner row'. Large luxury liners docked there, the first being 'Normandy' in 1935, of the French State line C.G.T. on its maiden voyage, followed by the 'Queen Mary' of the British Cunard line in 1936. Both ships were the world's largest passenger ships of their time. The large passenger ships of Norddeutscher Lloyd and Hapag and the Italian luxury liner of S.A. Italia also docked at the Finger piers. This diorama is produced from a photo from 1939, and shows the following ships from bottom to top:
Passenger steamer 'Resolute' of Hapag,
Fast steamer 'Hamburg' of Hapag,
Fast steamer 'Bremen' of Norddeutscher Lloyd,

Diorama of
'The stopping
distance of
ships'

Fast steamer, 'Columbus' of Norddeutscher Lloyd,

Fast steamer 'De Grasse' of Cie.G & I.Transatlantique,

Fast steamer 'Normandie' of Cie.G & I.Transatlantique, passenger motor ship 'Britannic' of the Cunard line,

Fast steamer 'Aquitania' of the Cunard line,

Fast steamship 'Conte di Savoia' of Italia S.A.,

Fast steamer 'Monarch of Bermuda' of the Furness line; Model maker: Dr. Hans Mehl

Diorama 'Helgoland'

The paper model of the island of Heligoland, built on a scale of 1:1,250 between 2001 and 2013, is modelled on over 2,000 photographs from the years 1890–1914, as well as a map of the island from 1891. Based on these extensive materials, the model builder Heinz-Peter Weiß succeeded in faithfully reproducing every street and every constructed building (there are over a thousand in total). In the barracks of the

model, a British crew team can be seen. It was only in 1890 that Britain ceded Heligoland in exchange for the island of Zanzibar, to the German Reich. Heinz-Peter Weiß refers to the Heligoland model as his life's work.

6 DEVELOPMENT OF MERCHANT SHIPS AND WAR SHIPS

The display cases show different types of merchant ships and a selection of types of warships from different nations.

Diorama 'The stopping distance of ships'

To avoid collisions at sea, the International Maritime Organisation IMO (International Maritime Organisation) has laid down regulations on stopping distances for ships. According to this, the stopping distance should not exceed 15 times the ship's length, after the manoeuvre from 'full ahead' to 'full back'. For a super tanker with a length of 375 metres, the stopping distance is around 5.6 km. However, in practice it is significantly below this. Thanks to the long-range detection of ships or obstacles by radar, captains are in the possession of good means to avoid collisions by rudder manoeuvres. Using three types of ships, the model shows how different stopping distances can turn out to be. Model maker: Dr. Hans Mehl

Installation 'A sea view from 2,000 metres high'

The simulated view from the control car of an airship at 2,000 metres above sea level shows how a airship navigator sees ships on the sea. From this altitude the ships seem to be the size of a 1:1,250 model.

Training boxes for ship recognition
To train pilots in ship recognition models were made in different scales to simulate reconnaissance flights from different heights. Main target of such training was for the pilots to distinguish between enemy ships and their own. scale 1:1,250.

Ship recognition
Waterline models of ships in the scales of 1:1200 and 1:1,250 were used for tactical training and ship recognition in many navies and air forces of the world.

They were made for this purpose in their thousands in the United States, Great Britain and Germany. Only rarely did reconnaissance aircraft succeed in photographing an enemy ship, on-side and undistorted. This was often due to bad weather or camouflage. Comparision with the silhouettes in their manuals thus was difficult for the pilots. The advantage of the three-dimensional models was that they could be studied from different angles.

Tactical situation display with ship models
The naval forces of the GDR (1956–1990) also used miniature ships for tactical training. In the example on view here ships from the West (blue) confront ships from the East (red).

The Japanese battleship 'Nagato' from different perspectives not the photo to the right
A ship changes its silhouette with each turn. Here is the Japanese battleship 'Nagato' from the side (0) and at angles of 45 and 60 degrees.

In the Royal Navy training during World Wars I & II was conducted using models by Basset-Lowke, Northampton. The German navy used models from Wiking Modellbau, Berlin. and the USA after entering World War II placed an order over 50,000 models

of japanese, german and italian navy and merchant ships with Comet Metal Works, New York.

7 WORKS OF ART AND WORLD CHAMPION MODELS

In model ship building there are competitions for the World Championship. The organiser is Naviga, the international governing body of ship model builders. Some of the models presented here are award-winning models. Delicate resin moulded models of all kinds of historic sailing ships are on display in the left cabinet. Their fine sails were made of Japanese silk. The miniatures in the right display cabinet by Michael Wünschmann, cast in metal, are similarly elaborate. The attention to detail ist astonishing. The model of the battleship Yamato (in the middle of the right cabinet) deserves special mention. It won Michael Wünschmann a Naviga gold medal in the class 4 (scale of 1.1,250) in the 1980s. The model displays the Yamato in April 1945 with the crew visible on deck and realistically looking rust stains run all over the ships hull. Michael Wünschmann is regarded as a perfectionist among model makers. 'Wünschmann model' is actually a term used among collectors.

Model of a Galleon, model maker: Wilhelm Heinrich

Battleship Yamato, model maker: Michael Wünschmann

Wooden handicrafts

After World War II there were no ship miniatures availlable due to shortage in raw materials. Except from Wiking some manufacturers built models from wood. Otto Heinz Henningsen, H. Stelling and some English model makers produced prototypical wooden models which are considered rarities today.

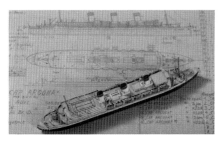

Handicrafts from paper

Miniature ship models from paper in the scale of 1:1,250 are a speciality of the model maker Heinz-Peter Weiß. He

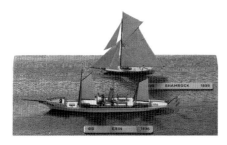

built the diorama of Heligoland mentioned on page 189. He has created true masterpieces from paper. His works are amongst the highlights of some of today's collections.

Köster models

'Köster ships' were, like the Wiking models produced in Germany during the 1930s. However, they were not cast in metal, but wooden models in a scale of 1:250 to 1:400. Edmund Köster's workshop, with over 20 employees was located in Hamburg. The focus was – unlike with Wiking – also on making large dioramas for authorities, museums and special designs for shipping and the fishing industry. The resulting 1936–37 diorama of the port of Hamburg in the scale of 1:400 extending over 75 square meters, was a masterpiece. There are only two other other Köster Dioramas left today and they are depicting fishing ports. They are prominently displayed in museums.

For collectors, the appeal of 'Köster ships' was in the multitude of lovingly crafted port and river vessels that were available in toy shops. Here they are assembled to form a fititious port model. Concerning navies Köster confined themselfes to the German Navy, who like the Maritime Casualty Investigation Board and the Port Authorities used their models for nautical lessons.

The Blue Ribbon

This display case is devoted to the 'Blue Ribbon'. This trophy has been awarded since 1860 to every passenger ship that has crossed the North Atlantic Ocean between Great Britain and the United States in a new record time. The organisation of this prize remained informal for a long time. In 1935 a British parliamentarian, Harold K Hale donated a trophy, the 'Northatlantic Blue Riband Challenge Trophy', also known as the Hales trophy. German passenger ships won the Blue Ribbon six times: Between 1898 and 1933 'Kaiser Wilhelm der Große', 'Deutschland', 'Kronprinz Wilhelm', 'Kaiser Wilhelm II', and others. However, in passenger solicitation, attention of the shipping lines increasingly shifted from speed towards good accomodations. Most recently the passenger ship 'United States' of the United States Line won the 'Blue Ribbon' in 1952 with a record speed on its western course of 34.51 knots and on its eastern course of 35.59 knots.

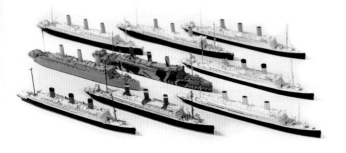

8 MODELS OF VARIOUS STANDARDS

Over time, ship miniatures were also built in scales other than 1:1,250 and subsequently got collected. Although there are no fixed rules for the production of these models, the standard scales used for railway models HO (1:87), N (1:160), and Z (1:220) are mainly used, as well as scales 1:400, 1:500 and 1:700. These models depict both historical aka traditional and present day ship types.

9 INLAND WATERWAY TRANSPORT AND HARBOR MANAGEMENT

INLAND WATERWAY TRANSPORT
From barge to pushed barge train
Inland waterway transport has a history of an amazing variety of ships and boats. Estimates say that in Europe from the 17th to the 20th century alone, there were a thousand different kinds of vehicles. This was due to regional isolations and geographical features of the waters. Only with the advent of supraregional transport connections, canals and the straightening of rivers, did the amount of vehicle types decrease. Bridges and locks required further standardisation.
In recent decades, freight transport on inland waterways has been reduced to a few types of cargo and transport techniques.

Ballin's 'Big steamer'
Albert Ballin was Director-General of Hapag (Hamburg-Amerikanische Packetfahrt-Actien Gesellschaft) and made this company the top cruise line in the world. He gave orders for three 'sea giants' to German shipyards. The ships did not reach high speed, but were lavishly equipped and set new standards for North Atlantic travel. First the 'Imperator' was finished in 1913, which was the largest passenger ship in the world with 52,117 BRT (The 'Titanic' had 46,329 BRT). It was followed by the 'Vaterland' with 54,282 BRT in 1914. The 'Bismarck' at 56,551 BRT, remained unfinished, and was only completed in 1920. All three ships had to be passed over to the allies after the First World War. The 'Imperator' became the 'Berengaria' in service for the Cunard line, the 'Vaterland' travelled as 'Leviathan' for the United States Line. The 'Bismarck' was initially renamed 'Majestic' and ran as 'Caledonia' from 1937 for the Royal Navy.

Logistics lounge. The Kuehne + Nagel (AG & Co.) KG. designed area, invites you on a journey through the world of logistics.

Apart from a few special vehicles, it is mostly self-propelled barges for bulk or dangerous goods, as well as container ships, pushed barge trains and bunkering ships (ships which provide other ships with fuel). Also ferries and passenger ships have acquired great importance. At the beginning of the millennium, they were the largest group on German inland waterways, with over a thousand units – ahead of self-propelled barges.

Kölner Aak freighter (Keulsche Aak), 1531

The term Aak refers to a Dutch type of fishing boat and to an old river cargo boat. The cargo boat Aak is considered to be one of the prototypes for the cargo ships on the lower Rhine. Their most important features are their hull planks, which are raised to the ends of the ship. Aaken can be towed (towed from the shore), or can be sailed. Their load capacity is 40 to 80 tons. Scale of 1:25, Model maker: unknown

Pushing boat Hercules VI,
Germany 1978
Scale of 1:50, Model maker Giesbert Narozny senior

Passenger ship 'Sabino', 1908
Scale 1:75, Model maker: Anton Happach

River bulk carrier
Scale of 1:50, Model maker Giesbert Narozny senior

Sidewheel tug 'Neptune'
1925 Scale 1:75,
Model maker: Hans-Jürgen Meyer, Moers

River passenger ship 'Blücher', 1913
Scale 1:100, Model builder: Hans-Jürgen Meyer, Moers

River passenger ship 'Goethe', 1996 Scale
1:100, Model maker: Hans-Jürgen Meyer, Moers

PORT INDUSTRIES
The port of Hamburg – gateway to the world

The port of Hamburg can look back on a history of more than 800 years. A first small harbor existed as early as the 9th century when the Hammaburg was founded where a branch of the river Bille flows into the river Alster.

However, the 7th May 1189 is considered to be the birthday of the port of Hamburg. On this day, the residents of Hamburg, with a faked document from Emperor Barbarossa bestowed upon themselves tax exemption on the lower Elbe. As a member of the Hanseatic League, Hamburg acquired greater importance in trade from 1321, but nevertheless remained way behind Lübeck. That changed with the discovery of the Americas and the Sea route to India. Important trade flows then shivted westward to the North sea and into Atlantic Ocean, and Hamburg benefited from this. From 1866, the port of Hamburg, which was 104 km from the sea, was expanded into a tidal harbour. This meant that ships could come in regardless of the tide. More and more harbour basins were built, and the port moved further westward. Overseas trade with the United States, South America, and the German colonies made Hamburg a seaport of global importance. Through the Greater Hamburg Act of 1937, the Prussian cities of Harburg-Wilhelmsburg and Altona were joined with Hamburg. This endet the competition between the three port cities and allowed for a more extensive harbor planning. Today, the port of Hamburg has 41 km of quay walls and is by far the most important port in Germany. It is one of the world's largest and most modern terminals for containers and other commodities. Due to its excellent motorway, rail and inland waterway transport connections, it is also a gateway to the markets of Northern, Central and Eastern Europe.

Bucket-chain dredger 'Triton', 1941
Dredgers are used to deepen shipping channels and ship berths. The device can also be used for the extraction of sand in gravel pits.
Scale: 1:50,
Model maker: Christian Stührmann

Tug 'Bützfleeth', 1978
Scale 1:50, Model maker: G. Schmidt model construction, Flensburg

Tug 'Bützfleeth'

The Hamburg Port Authority (HPA)
was established in 2005 as a result of pooling of harbor-related functions of different agencies*. Historically it goes back to the Düpe-Commission (Düpe = depth) from 1555, which had to supervise the navigable waters in the harbor and had to ensure sufficient water depth. In 1814 the Commission evolved into the Shipping and Harbor Deputation from which in 1863 the Bureau for River and Harbor Construction emerged. As a public-law institution HPA today runs a one-stop future-oriented and commercially oriented harbor management. Parts of HPA also take over responsibilities of public administration. An important field of duties is the development of the harbor. Besides providing a range of services including counseling one of the fundamental functions of HPA is the exertion of responsibilities towards the harbor's customers which are regulated by public law. This is conducted by networking closely with the authorities. Besides this, HPA is responsible for the infrastructure of the harbor, especially port railway, and the network of roads and bridges. The Harbor Master's Office which also belongs to HPA is responsible for the nautical safety within the harbor. The area of responsibility of the Harbor Master's Office with respect to harbor- and shipping laws extends from the harbor to all branches of the river Elbe and all waters connected to them between Oortkaten and Hamburg's state boundary at Tinsdal. The Hamburg Storm Tide Watch Service (WADI) is also part of HPA. It evaluates different meteorological data and water levels and issus exact forecasts for the advent of the flood rise at the harbor. In case of a heavy storm surge (4,5 meters above sea level and

Highlight: Model of the survey ship 'Schaarhörn' (1908): The Schaarhörn is the first ship to be recorded in the Hamburg monument list. The quality of the model is impressive.

Survey ship 'Schaarhörn' (1908)
The task of surveying vessels was the measurement of water depth using sonar. The 'Schaarhörn's' territory was the port of Hamburg. In World War I it served as a minesweeper, in World War II, she helped in the evacuation of refugees in the Baltic Sea. In 1993 it was recorded as the first ship in the Hamburg monument list.
Scale 1:75, model maker: Anton Happach

painter. During World War I he joined the German Imperial Navy. Until the end of the War he was employed at the Imperial Navy as a marine painter. In the early 1920s, Robert Schmidt-Hamburg worked as a full-time marine painter in Laboe. He carried out several study trips. He painted ports and ocean liners, tall ships, sea battles and coastal landscapes. The Kiel fjord was one of his favourite themes. The artist died in Laboe on 15 April 1963.

rising) HPA staff members cable forecasts and warnings to companies located in the harbor and to the authorities.

Bust of Johannes Dalmann

Johannes Dalmann (1823–1875) was the director of water engineering in Hamburg from 1857 and crucial in the transformation of the harbor into an open tidal port.

Diving helmet and suit

Divers worked in harbor basins wearing suits like this. Their tasks included the maintenance of sheet piling and the cleaning of debris after World War II. Diving operations are still carried out today in the port for security purposes, albeit with different equipment.

PAINTINGS

Robert Schmidt-Hamburg (1885–1963)
Raising a ship
sign. l.l.: 'R. Schmidt-Hamburg' Tempera
Robert Schmidt-Hamburg was born in Berlin on 5 April 1885. He initially worked at sea for various shipping companies, then later as a quartermaster (steerer). He used his spare time to train himself as a

Johannes Hubertus Hendrikus Bévort (1917–1996)
The port of Hamburg,
sign. l. r.: 'Bévort' Oil on canvas
The eyes are drawn to the middle of the harbour basin, where on both the left and right, large ships are at anchor. A tug is also visible in the foreground and extending over the water is a cloudy sky. Strong light-dark contrast in a color spectrum of grey and blue supplemented with a little red and yellow, along with a differentiated paint application applied partly with a spatula gives a harsh and powerful character to the harbour view. Johannes H. H. Bévort was born in 1917 in Utrecht. He was known for his depictions of naturalistic landscapes using his characteristic spatula technique.

Longitudinal view of Elbtunnel St. Pauli – Steinwärder
created by Philipp Holzmann & Cie., Frankfurt a. M. (illegible signature)

Willy Stöwer

(1864–1931)

Arrival of the 'Cap Polonio' in the port of Hamburg

sign. and dated l. r. '22.10.1922 Willy Stöwer' mixed media

Although he had already surpassed the peak of his career, the marine painter Willy Stöwer created one of his most beautiful paintings in 1922: 'Arrival of the 'Cap Polonio' in the port of Hamburg': The viewer stands at the height of the St. Pauli gangplanks and sees the 'Cap Polonio' approaching. A harbour tug has taken the bow hawser of the passenger steamer and helps it manoeuvre the narrow fairway. It is evening, but there is still ship traffic on the River Elbe: Right a small steam tug, left at the back, two barges. A police boat crosses the stream, on the left an Elbe ship sails by. On the opposite shore you can see the shipyard of Blohm and Voss, a steamer lies in the floating dock. On the right, the picture is framed by factory on the banks of Altona. It is slightly hazy, the last rays of the sun illuminate the scene and are reflected by the water.

Dusk has already set in. Willy Stöwer was born on May 22, 1864, in the old sea port of Wolgast. He was a self-taught artist. For several years he worked as an engineer in the design offices of various shipyards. Alongside this, he worked as an illustrator. Around 1890, he began his career as a free-lance artist. Willy Stöwer took part in several of Wilhelms II's Mediterranean travels and two of his trips to Norway. The travel images were always exhibited at the beginning of the following year at the Schulte art salon in Berlin. In 1898 Stöwer became a founding member of the German Navy League. In 1907 he received the title of Professor. In 1915 he was a war artist in Flanders, and in the same year a permanent exhibition of his paintings was opened in Swinemünde. After the abdication of the Emperor, the period of his success came to an end. Willy Stöwer died on May 31, 1931 in Tegel near Berlin. The 'Cap Polonio' was built at Blohm and Voss in 1914. From 1922, she sailed the route between Hamburg and the ports of La Plata. The ship was scrapped in 1935.

THE FOUNDER:
PROF. PETER TAMM

The fundus of the International Maritime Museum Hamburg is based upon the collection of Peter Tamm which today is run by a foundation in his name. The Hamburg native is a graduate economist and journalist, who led the Springer Publishing House for many years as chairman.

In 1934 when he was only 6 years old his love for everything maritime was decisively triggered when he was presented a miniature model of a coaster. But even before this formative moment the young boy showed a distinct interest in ships. At 5 years old he witnessed the launch of the sailing ship Gorch Fock (1933) at Blohm+-Voss and he accompanied his father to the port on numerous occasions which at the time was characterized by steamships, general cargo and hard physical work.

'The variety of smells and noises, the large ships that travelled to foreign countries, became a defining experience for me', recalled Peter Tamm later. After a carefree childhood, the young teenager experienced terrifying hours and nights in the air-raid shelter during the war in 1943. Large parts of Hamburg were destroyed by allied air strikes. Peter Tamms home however was not hit, and also during his short time in the Navy as a naval cadet, the young Peter Tamm was lucky: He survived the war unharmed. In 1948 after completing his studies, he started employment as editor of the Hamburger Abendblatt newspaper. He described how this came about in a 2010 interview: 'When I heard about the upcoming establishment of the Abendblatt, I had an idea. It was basically the only idea of my life, but it has survived until today, up to the establishment of my museum. I suggested to Otto Siemer, who was later to become Chief Editor, that I write a series of articles about the whereabouts of the famous old Hamburg ships. For the first few years after the war, people were fighting for survival, but in 1948 they started to show an interest again in such things. The series ran for a year, always on the last page at the bottom left. People cut it out and collected it.'

From then on, Peter Tamm remained connected to the Publisher as well as to its founder, Axel Springer. The then young journalist was there from the outset as the Hamburg Publisher built up the largest newspaper in Europe. Tamm admired Springer's entrepreneurial courage, his flair for the media business, and also his support for German unity. 'I owe almost everything to Axel Springer,' says Peter Tamm today, 'without him, I would not have been able to amass my collection to this magnitude and without him my museum would not have come into existence either.'

In return, Axel Springer recognised Tamm's special abilities and incorporated him in the management of his publishing house.

Peter Tamm started his career as an editor of the Hamburger Abendblatt. The picture on the right shows him with the publisher Axel Springer

Peter Tamm rose from editing to management, and in he became Chairman of the Board and remained in this position until 1991. He was enthusiastic professionally, and in his leisure time studied auction catalogues, historical documents, and maritime artefacts. The subsequent purchase of many of those objects resulted in an ever increasing collection. By the 1980s it had reached such a magnitude that it began to loose its merely private character.

In 1988, when he was sixty years old, Peter Tamm had the opportunity to acquire the heavily run-down former Park Hotel at 277 Elbchaussee, where he was finally able to show his treasures in suitable rooms.

At eighty years old, an age at which others have long since retired, he finally embarked on yet another step for his collection: He endowed his maritime treasures into a foundation finally enabeling a Maritime Museum to be founded in Hamburg – a city so closely tied to the sea.

Peter Tamm has been married to his wife, Ursula since 1958. The couple has four children and eight grandchildren. Peter Tamm has been honoured with many national and international medals and awards. He received an honorary degree from a Swedish University and an Honorary Professorship in Hamburg. He was appointed as honorary captain of the sailing ship 'Rickmer Rickmers' and has been a member of Deutsche Krebshilfe, the German Cancer charity, for decades. Today, at the age of 88, Peter Tamm is still active with his collection and can be found most days in his office at the museum.

Peter Tamm
can look back with satisfaction on his life as a manager, collector and committed citizen.

The building at Elbchaussee hosted the Peter Tamm collection and his private Scientific Institute of shipping and naval history between 1991–2008

THE HISTORY OF
THE COLLECTION OF PETER TAMM.

For decades, Peter Tamm has collected literally everything that is connected to seafaring and its history: Models, paintings, nautical charts, construction plans, equipment, uniforms, books, documents, and more. As a successful manager and later director of Axel Springer AG, he had the means to pursue this passion. He succeeded in gathered the largest private maritime collection in the world.

By the end of the 1980s, it extended beyond the capacity of his home. A visitor described his impression: 'In Tamm's house, there was practically no corner, not a square centimetre of wall anymore that was free of maritime images, items, books, that caused his wife Ursula more problems than just dusting.' Consequently, the collector started looking for larger rooms. In 1988, he acquired the former 'Park Hotel Teufelsbrück' on the Elbe and moved in with his collection. In the same year, he founded his private scientific Institute for Maritime and Naval history (WISM) and employed a number of experts for the different subjects of his collection.

The collection aims to document the history of seafaring, from its beginnings until the present. This is not an end in itself for Peter Tamm; he is convinced that with each exhibit, the experiences of the past can be unveiled for the present.

Even ordinary relics have a special meaning. A uniform cap, a yellowed officer patent or a menu from an ocean liner could be traded at the flea market as a curiosity. However, when such objects enter the Tamm collection, they become important piece in a larger picture.

'A collector', recalls Peter Tamm, 'cannot escape his fate. There are many families, many estates. Their heirs don't want anything to be lost, and so increasing quantities are being sent to my address.' Often, the large table in the lounge of Elbchaussee was overflowing with models, documents, books and maps. Everything then had to be archived and catalogued: a task for the staff of the Scientific Institute for Marine and Naval history.

Since the 1980s objects were given on loan to significant axhibitions in other museums such as the German Historic Museum in Berlin or the Altona Museum in Hamburg. Several exhibits from the Tamm collection were also part of the spectacularly successfull Titanic exhibition which in 1997 attracted 1.2 Million visitors. Also the annual 'art maritim', which was designed by the WISM with alternating partner countries, was part of the fixed programme at the Hanseboot fair until 2006.

With an increasing collection the question of a new site arose to keep things on public display as the mansion at Elbchaussee with its magnificent view of the river Elbe was not a public museum. Whoever was interested could sign up for a visit.

At least 30,000 people per year came. At the same time, Peter Tamm amongst many many others began to wonder why Hamburg, as one of the world's most important port cities, had no maritime museum. The city soon expressend interest i such a project. Mayors Henning Voscherau and Ortwin Runde encouraged Peter Tamm in his ideas for a foundation. The Finance Senator Dr. Wolfgang Peiner and the Gert Hinnerk Behlmer, head of the Ministry of Culture, also played important roles. Together with Peter Tamm, they investigated several properties for their suitability for a future Museum. 'When we visited Kaispeicher B', remembered Wolfgang Peiner later, 'I noticed it was like a bolt of lightning went through Peter Tamm. It was spontaneous enthusiasm, although it was clear to both of us how difficult it would be. Because a storehouse is just a storehouse and not a museum.' But Peter Tamm refused to let Kaispeicher B go, after all, it is not only the oldest surviving structure of the port of Hamburg, but is also located where Hamburg is shaping its future: at the entrance to the new quartier 'Hafencity' (harbour city). In 2003, the Mayor of Hamburg Ole von Beust, announced that the Senate would grant the Peter Tamm Foundation a 99-year leasehold for Kaispeicher B. At the same time, the city renovated the building for 30 million euros, a measure that would have been necessary anyway to save the heritage protected building from decay. Peter Tamm stated on the other hand, that the Museum could manage without public funds, and at the same time, donated his collection in the form of a private foundation to the city.

In 2008, the International Maritime Museum Hamburg was opened in the presence of German Federal President Horst Köhler. Since then, it has attracted hundreds of thousands of visitors from all over the world.

Historic picture of Kaispeicher B, today headquarters of the Peter Tamm Foundation

THE BUILDING
FROM STORE TO MUSEUM

With the historic Kaispeicher B building, the International Maritime Museum has found a both worthy and appropriate site. This towering monolith brick building, situated on the edge of the Speicherstadt district, is under monument protection. It connects the historic Speicherstadt, recognised in 2015 as world cultural heritage site by UNESCO, with the modern Hafencity.

The former storehouse is flanked by water on two sides. When commodities arrived side-on Kaispeicher B in the 'Magdeburger Hafen' (Magdeburg harbour) they were hoisted onto the floors using external winches. Goods up for the further transport handled side-on 'Brooktorhafen' (Brooktor harbour), where barges could access the Kaispeicher directly. There was even a railway connection. The store, built in 1878-79, was the first pure warehouse located here and a precursor to the Speicherstadt warehouse district, the construction of which began ten years later. Kaispeicher B was built by the architects Bernhard Georg Jacob Hanssen and Wilhelm Emil Meerwein in neo-Gothic style.

Because of the sophisticated design of its facade with Gothic pointed arches, gables and wall panels, this functional architecture imposed a prestigious sight. The construction of the building, like the entire Speicherstadt, consists of a load-bearing internal frame of wood and steel columns, as well as load-bearing exterior walls. The building was originally designed as a combination of silo storage for grain and ground storage for general cargo – a combination unique to Hamburg. However the concept didn't really work. In 1884, only six years after its construction, floors were inserted into the silo section. This modification resulted in nine floors in the larger eastern section, compared to only eight floors in the western, yet with the same roof and eaves height. This explains the height gap between floors, which meets the visitors to the exhibition. Grain however continued to be stored here, but in single berths on the storage floors. The guide rails that divided these cells have been preserved in parts. Since the recent renovation of Kaispeicher B an area of 11,500 square metres is available for exhibitions.

In the year 2000, the building was placed under monument protection, and until the end of 2003 it was used as a general cargo warehouse. The plans for the renovation starting in 2005 were developed by the Hamburg architect, Mirjana Markovic. She incorporated four 'airspaces' (plenums) into the building each of them

A worthy location for the museum: The old store, directly on the water front.

interconnecting three floors. A pedestrian bridge from the north an a public passage through the building link the museum to its vivinity. On the ground floor of the museum there are a café a restaurant and a museums shop. The construction work itself proved to be costly, as conservational requirements had to be combined with the requirements of exhibition architecture. Elevators, air-conditioning and sprinklers had to be sensitively integrated, and old columns made of wood and iron had to be restored. More than 150 construction workers individually chiselled out around 50,000 bricks from the exterior walls and the facade, examined them, worked on them and inserted them again. More than 2,000 cubic meters of concrete and 150 tons of reinforced steel had to be used without ruining the atmosphere of the old store. The topping-out ceremony was celebrated by the Peter Tamm Foundation on May 12, 2006; the building was approved and finished on December 21, 2006. From now on the International Maritime Museum gradually moved in.

The historic wooden structures shown here before the collection was moved in, were widely preserved. Kaispeicher B is protected by a preservation order.

Das Internationale Maritime

Senator a. D. Dr. Wolfgang Peiner

Germanischer Lloyd AG

STIFTUNG MARITIM

Ulf Gänger

Hamburg Süd

Petra und Joachim Herz

ORIO

Georg W. Claussen

De

Deutsche Shipping

HSH Nordbank AG

P

Bert

Deutsche Bahn AG

Marqu

Mabanaft Gmb

Otto Wulff Bauunternehmung

Nikolaus W. Schües & Nikolaus H. Schües, Partner i. Fa. F. Laeisz

Bernhard Schulte GmbH & Co. KG

Deutsche Schiffsbank AG

capiton AG

Reederei Claus-Peter Offen

H. Wolff

Deutsche Afrika - Linien
John T. Essberger
Freundeskreis des IMMH e.V.

n Hamburg dankt seinen Stiftern und Freunden

& Milena Ebel

Gebr. Heinemann

e Dampfschifffahrts-Gesellschaft KG

Le nhardt & Blumberg Reederei

GmbH & Co. KG Stephan Reith

Ernst Peter Komrowski

Peter Döhle Schiffahrts-KG

ng Denkmalschutz   Hapag-Lloyd AG

Klaus-Michael Kühne Stiftung

Hamburger Sparkasse

Verwaltungsgesellschaft ICL Holding mbH

Hans-Otto und Engelke Schümann

AXEL SPRINGER STIFTUNG

lan und Barbara Karan-Stiftung

Eberhard Wienholt

Erck Rickmers

kmers

AG

**One founder,
many supporters:**
The International
Maritime Museum
of Hamburg thanks
all its Friends and
sponsors.

LIBRARY AND READING ROOM

The library of the International Maritime Museum Hamburg has been open to visitors since 1 April 2015. It is located in the Gebr. Heinemann Wing of the Museum. Its wide range of topics includes merchant shipping, naval history, cartography, navigation, ship construction since its earliest beginnings in the 17th century, research and journeys of discovery and also marine painters. In addition, there are works of fiction, encyclopaedias, dictionaries, current and older journals and shipping registers. After registration, the reading room of the library is accessible to all interested people for a small fee.

Opening hours:
Wednesdays, 10:30 am to 3:00 pm

IT WON'T WORK WITHOUT FRIENDS

The International Maritime Museum's Circle of Friends, supports the Museum in its efforts to be an independent commercially run endeavour in the cultural sector of the city of Hamburg and to preserve history. The goals of the Museum and the Foundation can only be achieved if we work together, as a team of employees and Friends of the Museum. That is why we would be delighted if you became a member of the Circle of Friends and help us with:

- the preservation, study and promotion of maritime history, because it is human and cultural history,
- to maintain and develop the IMMH in the historic Kaispeicher B building as a living place of history,
- to present this unique collection from all angles to the public, even more effectively,

In the Reading Room of the library, there is access to a rich collection of books and historic maps and documents for anyone who is interested.

- to enable further expansion, and support special exhibitions and holiday programmes,
- and as a member of the Circle of Friends to act as an ambassador for the Museum.

Your financial and personal commitment in the Circle of Friends guarantees the preservation and the further development of this unique museum project.
As a member of the Circle of Friends you will

- enjoy free admission to the Museum
- can participate in exclusive events and guided tours
- will receive invitations to special events
- learn of important information first-hand
- will be in close contact with the Museum's employees and in dialogue with like-minded people

Circle of Friends
International
Maritime Museum Hamburg
Koreastr. 1
20457 Hamburg
Tel: + 49 (0) 40 300 92 30-14
Fax + 49 (0) 40 300 92 30 45
E-Mail: freundeskreis@peter-tamm-sen.de
www.imm-hamburg.de

IMPRINT

Author:
Christian Tröster
with the assistance of
Dr. Axel Grießmer
Manfred Meyer
Dr. Gudrun Müller
Gerrit Menzel
Holger Freiherr von Neuhoff
Dr. Hans Mehl
Hans-Jürgen Steffen

Photos:
Michael Zapf

Painting reproductions:
Alan Ginsburg

Photo credits:
Axel Springer Verlag, p. 5
Courtesy of the Osher Map Library,
University of Southern Maine, p. 28
Katharina Marg, p. 53 a.
MK timelapse GmbH, p. 75 (4)
Tillman Straszburger p. 6/7
Manfred Stein p. 175 (1), 177 (2), 179 (1)

© 2015
**by Koehlers Verlagsgesellschaft
Hamburg**
A company of Tamm media
all rights reserved

Publishing
Stephan Alpen LTG.

Design and production:
Peter Plasberg,
Sozietät für Kommunikation, Hamburg

Printing and Binding:
Gorenjski tisk, Slovenia

We would be happy to send you a complete list of available titles.
Please send an email with your address to: vertrieb@koehler-books.de
You will find us on the Internet at www.koehler-books.de

Bibliographic information
of the German National Library
The German National Library
lists this publication in the
German National Bibliography;
detailed bibliographic data is
available on the Internet at
http://dnb.d-nb.de

ISBN: 978-3-7822-1258-8